Concepts in Chemistry

An Introduction to Chromatography

Second Edition

By David Abbott
Concise Certificate Chemistry
Revision Chemistry for Sixth Forms

An Introduction to Chromatography

Second Edition

by
David Abbott and R. S. Andrews

Longman

LONGMAN GROUP LTD
London

Associated companies, branches and representatives throughout the world

First edition © David Abbott and R. S. Andrews 1965
Second edition © Longman Group Ltd 1970

First published 1965
Second edition 1970
Second impression 1970

ISBN 0 582 32194 8

Printed and Bound in Great Britain by
Hazell, Watson & Viney Ltd
Aylesbury, Bucks

Preface to Second Edition

Chromatography is now firmly established as a major analytical and preparative tool, invaluable in the chemical, biological and medical sciences and widely used in industry. Despite this pre-eminence, however, the theoretical background and the actual apparatus required, even for quite advanced work, is very simple, so that this is an ideal subject for science courses in schools, universities and technical colleges. Experiments are actually fun, so even non-scientists will find chromatography a fascinating addition to their curriculum.

This book is suitable for both Ordinary and Advanced level studies.

In preparing the second edition of the book, the authors have tried to continue their aim of producing a true introduction to the whole subject of chromatography, and have therefore included most of the recent innovations in this field. Because this is a practical subject they are delighted to include for the first time a range of plates covering commercial apparatus and media. They would like to express their sincere thanks to the following firms whose cooperation and financial assistance have made this possible: Aimer Products, Baird & Tatlock, CAMAG, Camlab, Field Instruments, Joyce Loebl, Kodak, LKB Instruments, Perkin-Elmer, Quickfit & Quartz, H. Reeve Angel, Shandon Scientific, and Waters Associates. Our thanks also go to many other individuals for their help.

David Abbott   R. S. Andrews

Contents

1 Introduction to Chromatography

You will all be familiar with the methods used to separate simple mixtures of chemical substances. Perhaps you have at some time or another attempted to separate a mixture of powdered sulphur and iron filings. All that is needed here is a magnet which selectively removes the iron filings from the mixture leaving the sulphur unaffected. As the individual components of a mixture get more and more similar in physical or chemical properties, it becomes increasingly difficult to separate them. Thus, acetone (boiling point 58°C) and water (boiling point 100°C) can be separated fairly easily by fractional distillation. On the other hand, it is a much more difficult task to separate the components of liquid air by fractional distillation because liquid oxygen has a boiling point of −183°C and liquid nitrogen −196°C; the boiling points of the Rare Gases lie very close to these values.

In chemistry and biology it is frequently necessary to separate, isolate, purify and identify the components of mixtures much more complex than the ones mentioned above. For example, when a protein (such as wool, egg albumin or the casein of milk) is heated with dilute mineral acid it is broken down (hydrolysed) to give a complex mixture of amino acids, the individual components of which resemble one another very closely in chemical and physical properties. It would be an almost impossible task to separate the components by a method such as fractional crystallisation. It is possible, however, to achieve such a separation fairly rapidly by the process of *chromatography*. Chromatography can be defined as that technique for the separation of a mixture of solutes in which separation is brought about by the differential movement of the individual solutes through a porous medium under the influence of a moving solvent.

The Russian biologist Tswett was probably the first person to appreciate the possibilities of such a method as long ago as 1906. The porous medium he used consisted of finely powdered chalk packed into a long vertical glass column provided with an outlet at the bottom. He noticed that when a solution of green plant pigments was applied to the top of the column and then washed down with light petroleum, a series of horizontal bands of the different pigments began to separate from one another as they moved down the column. The term chromatography, which literally means 'colour writing', was coined to describe this phenomenon. In actual fact the separation had nothing to do with the compounds being coloured, but was simply due to the fact that the various pigments had different adsorptive affinities for the chalk, those least strongly adsorbed moving down the column more rapidly than those more strongly adsorbed. His experiment, then, was probably the first demonstration of *adsorption column chromatography*.

Although Tswett investigated this phenomenon further it remained more or less a laboratory curiosity until Martin and Synge introduced *partition column chromatography*. The medium used in their columns contained a certain amount of water and the separation which they achieved depended on the continuous distribution or partition of the components of the mixture applied to the column between the water held on the medium and the solvent flowing down the column. Separations by partition chromatography are particularly suitable for water-soluble compounds, so this development greatly extended the range of chromatography to include many substances of biological importance.

With the closed columns, however, it was very difficult to obtain a reliable identification of very small quantities of the separated substances, and later, in 1944, when Consden, Gordon, and Martin described *paper chromatography* in which separations are achieved (mainly by partition) on sheets of filter paper, the full advantages of an 'open column' system were appreciated. With paper chromatography quantities of the order of a few micrograms of most compounds could be detected and identified in a dependable manner.

Two important developments followed. Firstly the 'open column' concept was carried further by the introduction of *thin layer chromatography* in which separations are carried out with thin layers of almost any material supported on glass plates. The principle of the method was described over 25 years ago but it did not obtain universal support until Stahl standardised the procedure and showed its wide applications as recently as 1958.

The last of the chromatographic techniques, *gas chromatography*, was a logical development from column chromatography in which gas replaced liquid as the solvent. Because of this, separations have to be performed within the confines of a column. It is particularly valuable for separating mixtures of gases, or volatile liquids or solids, and has developed rapidly since Martin and James described their first experiments in 1952.

Today there is almost no field of chemistry or biology which does not use chromatography in some form. For example, chromatographic analysis is used in forensic medicine (as in the detection of poisons), in the examination of biological tissues and their related chemical processes (metabolic pathways), and structural studies on complex molecules such as carbohydrates, proteins and complicated phenols in plants. Chromatography is, of course, an important technique in inorganic as well as organic chemistry. It was as a result of the search for a suitable method of separating nuclear fission products that the first ion-exchange resins were developed.

2 The Theory of Materials used in Chromatography

At first sight the various systems used for chromatography, e.g. a sheet of filter paper, a glass plate covered with a thin layer of powder, or a glass column prepared for liquid or column chromatography, appear very simple. Yet with each of these it is possible to achieve separations which would be almost impossible by any other method. In each case a separation is dependent upon a multiple partition or adsorption-desorption process.

The success of chromatography depends upon the fact that during their passage through a chromatographic system, small differences in the partitioning or adsorption-desportion behaviour of each component in a mixture are multiplied manyfold. The greater this multiplication factor the greater the ease with which the components may be separated and the greater the resolution.

From the point of view of efficiency, chromatography is often compared with fractional distillation and the concept of theoretical plates applied. In distillation, a theoretical plate is that unit within the column where there can be considered to be an equilibrium between the ascending vapour and the descending liquid. Obviously the greater the number of these the greater will be the efficiency of fractionation.

Similarly, a chromatographic system can be considered as being made up of a series of such hypothetical plates, each one being a unit within the system in which equilibrium is established between the solvent and the material used in the system. The particular advantage of chromatography is that a very large number of theoretical plates, and hence high efficiency, can readily be achieved. Because equilibrium is rapidly established, highly efficient separations can often be carried out in a very short time.

2.1 Partition chromatography

Partition chromatography, as its name suggests, is a technique which involves the separation of mixtures of substances by means of partition between the moving solvent and a stationary liquid which is held on a suitable solid support. The solvent may be a liquid (*liquid/liquid chromatography*) or a gas (*gas/liquid chromatography*). Although from a theoretical point of view these techniques are very closely related, the practical details are quite different, and we shall therefore consider them separately.

Liquid/liquid chromatography

The most popular techniques of liquid/liquid separation are carried out on cellulose or moist silica gel, which may be in the form of sheets, thin layers or packed into columns. The medium in each case acts as a support for water. Partition chromatography of this type is therefore used mainly for the separation of water-soluble substances. Let us consider the separation of a mixture or substance on a sheet of filter paper as a typical example.

Filter paper is made from cellulose fibres which naturally contain a certain amount of water. We can consider that the individual parts of each fibre, together with their associated moisture, constitute minute (hypothetical) 'cells'. It is partition of the substances between the moisture in the cells and the solvent flowing over the cells which actually brings about a separation. The water in these cells remains stationary as the solvent moves over them and is therefore referred to as the *stationary phase*, while the solvent flowing down the paper is called the *moving phase*.

In true partition chromatography the only factor which influences the movement of a compound as the solvent travels along the paper is the relative solubility of that compound in the stationary and moving phases.

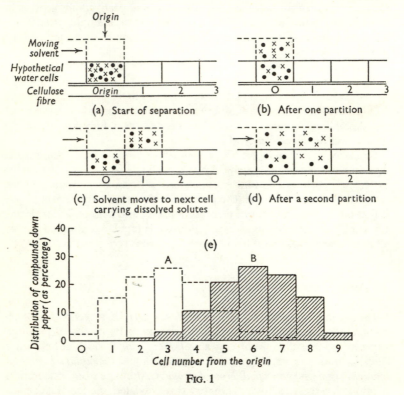

(a) Start of separation

(b) After one partition

(c) Solvent moves to next cell carrying dissolved solutes

(d) After a second partition

(e)

Fig. 1

Substances which are only soluble in the solvent will migrate the same distance as the solvent front whilst other compounds, which are soluble only in the water, will remain on the origin. In actual paper chromatography, other factors, such as adsorption, will influence the migrations.

It is most important to remember that the partition of a substance between two immiscible solvents is unaffected by the presence of other substances.

We can best illustrate these principles by reference to an example. Let us consider that a mixture of two compounds A and B (whose partition coefficients between the stationary and moving phases are 2:1 and 1:2 respectively, i.e. A is relatively more water soluble) is applied to the origin of a paper chromatogram. Fig. 1 shows diagrammatically a cross-section of the paper containing the mixture dissolved in the water of a cell on the origin. For convenience it can be considered that the partition takes place between equal volumes of the moving and stationary phases. In Fig. 1, molecules of compound A are represented by closed circles, those of B by crosses.

When the solvent just reaches the cell (this being when separation begins) the two substances will partition themselves according to the *partition law**.

The solvent containing a certain amount of the mixture will then move along the paper and will encounter another cell containing only water, while fresh solvent will come into contact with the original cell (Fig. 1(c)), and a further partition will take place (Fig. 1(d)). This process known as

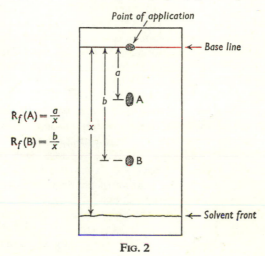

$$R_f(A) = \frac{a}{x}$$

$$R_f(B) = \frac{b}{x}$$

FIG. 2

countercurrent distribution continues as the solvent moves along the paper and Fig. 1(e) represents the distribution of A and B along the paper after ten such partitions. It is obvious that the two compounds have already started to separate. In practice, this process is repeated countless times, giving eventually a sharp separation of the two compounds.

The chromatogram which would result from the above separation is shown in Fig. 2. A will have moved one third of the distance moved by the solvent front while B has moved two thirds of this distance.

One of the most important features of chromatography is that with a given chromatographic system the movement of any compound relative to the solvent front is a reproducible and characteristic property. In the case of paper and thin layer chromatography the movement of any compound is most conveniently expressed as R_f or R_X values.

With columns, the R values do not have the same significance because

---

* If a solute A is soluble in two solvents B and C, A will distribute itself between B and C in accordance with the following law:

$$\frac{\text{Concentration of A in B}}{\text{Concentration of A in C}} = \frac{\text{a constant}}{\text{at}}\text{constant temperature} = \text{the partition coefficient}$$

one cannot usually determine the position of the solvent front or the compounds within the column, so that other criteria have to be used. These will be discussed later.

Although cellulose and silica gel act as supports for water in partition separations, their individual characteristics recommend one or other of them for particular applications.

Cellulose is a natural product usually derived from cotton. It is a polymer of glucose and thus contains a large number of hydroxyl (—OH) groups. It has a rather complicated microstructure. Products for chromatography are available in *fibrous* and *microgranular* forms (see Section 2.4), the latter being particularly suitable for thin layer chromatography. Cellulose is used for separations of water-soluble substances when adsorption is undesirable.

On the other hand *silica gel*, which is prepared by the action of concentrated hydrochloric acid on sodium silicate solution, has some adsorptive characteristics. Because of its inorganic nature, it is used when corrosive methods are going to be required for detection (as in thin layer chromatography), or more generally for the fractionation of less *polar* water-soluble substances when adsorption influences the result.

The concept of *polarity* introduced above is one which is commonly encountered, and it therefore warrants further description. Bascially polarity refers to the separation of charge within molecules, or the ionic character of molecules. Ionic compounds are therefore highly polar. Many covalent compounds, however, have a certain amount of ionic character since there is often an unequal sharing of bonding electrons within the molecule. In the case of water for example, the valency electrons spend, on average, much more time near the oxygen nucleus than near the hydrogen nuclei, with the result that the oxygen end of the molecule becomes negative and the hydrogen end positive. We can therefore say that water is a *polar* liquid.

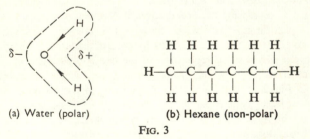

(a) Water (polar) (b) Hexane (non-polar)

Fig. 3

In the hexane molecule, on the other hand, the valency electrons are shared almost equally between the atoms involved in each bond, and there is virtually no charge separation within the molecule. Hexane is thus a typically *non-polar* liquid. Between water and hexane there are numerous other liquids with intermediate polarities. A selection of the more common ones is given in Table 1.

The value of this concept of polarity in chromatogrpahy is twofold. First, the polarity of substances greatly influences their behaviour in solution, and secondly the adsorptive character of molecules increases with increasing polarity.

Solids tend to dissolve only in liquids of similar polarity, so that polar solids dissolve in polar solvents such as water, non-polar substances dissolve in non-polar liquids such as hexane, and substances of medium polarity dissolve in solvents of medium polarity such as ethanol, ether, chloroform etc. Liquids are also miscible with other liquids of similar polarity (i.e. water with methanol and benzene with toluene).

The polarity of molecules depends upon the nature of their constituent atoms and the shape of the molecule. Groups such as —F, —OH, —NH$_2$, —Cl (decreasing in that order) tend to give rise to polar character, while the introduction of —CH$_2$— groups into organic compounds diminishes the polarity. Similarly, asymmetry in molecules produces increased polarity. Carbon tetrachloride has four fairly polar C—Cl bonds in the molecule, but because this is symmetrical, the molecule shows no net polarity. Carbon tetrachloride is therefore less polar than chloroform (CHCl$_3$) in which there is a small net separation.

Finally, it should be borne in mind that the polarity of substances increases when they are dissolved in polar solvents, so that the polarity of the components of a mixture might be much greater in liquid/liquid chromatography than it would be in, say, gas/liquid chromatography.

Gas/liquid chromatography (GLC)

The theoretical principles of GLC are closely similar to those described above. Separations depend upon the partition of solute molecules between a liquid, supported on a suitable solid, and the gas flowing through the system. For practical purposes, the liquid has to have very low volatility so the water-containing media used in liquid/liquid partition cannot be used.

The aim in this technique is to provide a thin liquid film, with as large an interface as possible between the gas and liquid phases to facilitate partition between them. The support should therefore have a high specific area. Many solids have this property but most are unsuitable because they exhibit adsorptive effects which interfere with separations.

The most popular support is derived from *celite*, a diatomaceous earth composed of the silica–containing bodies of millions of microscopic sea creatures. Celite is also mixed with clay and made into *firebricks*. By crushing, washing and grading the material from these bricks another useful support can be produced.

Much of the original work in GLC was concerned with non-polar substances such as the hydrocarbons in petrol. These are little affected by adsorption, and the firebrick powder was found to be easier to use than celite since it exists in larger, free-flowing aggregates which give a more rapid separation. For more polar substances, however, its adsorptive capacity is a disadvantage and celite is preferred.

Celite itself also exhibits adsorptive tendencies, which may be reduced by treatment with acids, alkali or by reacting with a suitable reagent to block the adsorbing sites. *Silanising*, which involves reacting the celite with reagents such as dimethyldichlorosilane, is very good for this purpose. Celite products that have received any combination of these treatments are readily available commercially.

For highest efficiency it is essential that the support should have only a fairly narrow range of particle sizes. This is achieved by careful sieving. As celite particles are fragile, they can easily be broken down to fine dust if treated badly. Celite supports should therefore be treated with care.

The choice of the involatile liquids for use in GLC depends upon the nature of the substances being separated, and the temperature at which the separation is going to be conducted. Usually the *stationary phase* is chosen to be of a similar chemical nature to the substances being separated. A whole range of substances is available to help in this choice, including amides, amines, hydrocarbon oils and greases, silicones, waxes, alcohols, ethers, polymers, polyesters and many others. Some supports combine the properties of a support and liquid phase all in one. An excellent example of this is the *Porapak* range, which is a product of Waters Associates Inc.

Porapak Q, which is the most commonly used, is a polymer produced from ethylvinylbenzene and divynlbenzene. Other types are modified to alter the properties, mainly the polarity.

The porous polymer beads have rigid structures and have the partition properties of a highly extended liquid without many of the problems associated with the normal coated supports.

Although the beads present a very large surface area, they still do not react with polar compounds such as water, alcohols, acids etc., and it is possible to obtain very sharp separations of these low retention times. A number of actual separations is shown in Plate 8.

Since there is no liquid phase to volatilise away slowly, separations are reproducible and, because the separation is based on partition only, large samples may be placed on the column without *tailing*. This makes the technique valuable for preparative and trace analysis chromatography.

The properties mentioned above make this material very useful for students.

2.2 Gel filtration chromatography

Gel filtration chromatography is a particular type of liquid/liquid chromatography for the separation of substances according to differences in the sizes of their molecules. It first became established as a laboratory technique with the introduction of the *Sephadex* range in 1959.

The Sephadex gel filtration media are produced from a polysaccharide, dextran, which is cross-linked to give a more or less uniform 3-dimensional network of dextran chains at the molecular level. At the macroscopic level the product is in the form of spherical beads. These can be seen in Plate 1. Because of their high content of hydroxyl groups, the beads have a great affinity for water and they therefore swell up in water or electrolyte solutions to give semi-transparent gel particles. These are normally packed into columns for chromaography.

A gel filtration separation occurs in the following manner. The sample being chromatographed is applied to the top of the column, and then washed slowly through the bed of gel particles with water or buffer solution. Substances with molecules larger than the largest pores of the swollen beads (above the *exclusion limit*) are not able to penetrate the gel particles and therefore pass through the bed in the liquid phase outside the particles and emerge from the bottom first.

Smaller molecules, however, are able to penetrate the particles to varying extents depending upon their shape and size. There is thus a partition of the molecules between the liquid *inside* the gel particles and that *outside*. The smaller the molecules, the greater the percentage of the liquid within the particles that is available to them.

Molecules therefore leave the column in the order of *decreasing* molecular size. Three stages in the separation of large molecules from small molecules are shown in Fig. 4. The large dots represent the large molecules, the small dots the small molecules, and the open circles the gel-filtration particles.

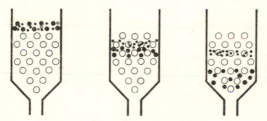

FIG. 4. A gel filtration separation

Although the term gel filtration is the most popular one for describing the above phenomenon, other terns such as *gel-permeation, molecular exclusion* and *molecular sieving* are also encountered in the literature.

A number of other media apart from the dextran-based gels is available for gel filtration in aqueous solution. The Bio-Gel series produced in the U.S.A., for example, is based on cross-linked polyacrylamide gels.

The fractionation range of these gels depends upon the pore size, and this in turn is inversely proportional to the amount of cross-linking agent used. The greater the amount of cross-linking agent the less the swelling properties of the gel.

The usual way of characterising the various types of gel is by means of their *water regain values*. This represents the amount of water (in ml) imbibed by 1g of the dry gel grains. The type numbers of the Sephadex and Bio-Gel series are ten times the water regain value; Sephadex G-10 has a water regain value of 1 and Sephadex G-200 a water regain value of 20. These values do not include the water between the grains.

The types with low water regains have the smallest pore size and are used for the fractionation of small molecules, while the types with high water regains are used for the fractionation of high molecular weight compounds. Thus G-10 will fractionate substances with molecular weights up to about 700, and G-200 will fractionate globular proteins and peptides with molecular weights ranging from 5 000 up to several hundred thousands. Other types cover the intermediate ranges.

For the fractionation of substances of really high molecular weights such as certain proteins, polysaccharides, nucleic acids and viruses, gel particles with even larger pore sizes are required. These are produced from a polysaccharide known as *agarose* which is a neutral polymer derived from agar.

Gel filtration has a number of applications. The most obvious is the analysis of mixtures of molecules of different molecular weight and size. The example in Plate 4(a) shows the separation of four low molecular weight substances, raffinose (M.W.504), maltose (M.W.342), glucose (M.W.180) and KCl on Sephadex G–15. The example in Plate 4(b) shows the separation of very high molecular weight virus particles on an agarose gel.

Another very valuable property of gel filtration is that it allows molecular weight determinations to be performed. Although fractionation really depends upon *molecular size*, extensive investigations have shown, for example, that the *elution volumes* of globular proteins on the G–100 and G–200 types are largely determined by their *molecular weight*. Over a considerable range, the elution volume is approximately a linear function of the logarithm of the molecular weight. If a calibration curve of proteins of known molecular weight can be drawn up, the molecular weight of unknown proteins can be determined even in crude preparations. This kind of approach is very valuable in enzyme work.

So far we have discussed gel filtration only in aqueous solutions. By using specially modified media, however, this technique can be extended to include separations with organic solvents.

One such product is derived from the dextran-based gels by reacting the hydrophilic hydroxyl groups with a reagent to render them hydrophobic. The modified gel particles then swell in non-aqueous solvents. Another product is derived from cross-linked polystyrene. Separations of lipids on these two media are shown in Plate 5.

The choice of the type of medium for gel filtration experiments is not the only criterion which has to be taken into account. When the gel beads are packed into small columns it has been found that coarse beads and high flow rates both lead to poor separations. The effect of particle size can be clearly seen in Plate 2.

Resolution can also be improved by a technique known as recycling chromatography. This is discussed in Section 5.6.

2.3 Adsorption chromatography

In adsorption chromatography, small differences in the adsorption-desorption behaviour of substances between a moving solvent (a liquid or a gas) and a stationary solid phase are utilised to achieve a separation. Adsorption is a surface phenomenon denoting a higher concentration at an interface than is present in the surrounding medium.

Adsorption should not be confused with absorbtion, which is the penetration of one substance into the bulk of another. Blotting paper absorbs ink and sponges absorb water.

Separations involving a liquid solvent are also classed as *liquid/solid chromatography*; those involving a gas as *gas/solid chromatography*.

Liquid/solid chromatography

Most of the solids which are used for thin layer or column chromatographic separations involving adsorption are metallic oxides, hydrated oxides and salts. The most popular are silica gel and alumina. Other adsorbents such as charcoal and polyamide (nylon) powder have specialised uses.

In a chromatographic sense the term adsorption is limited to interactions involving hydrogen bonding and weaker electrostatic forces. When the interactions are ionic in character the process is referred to as *ion-exchange*. We shall consider this in the next section.

The adsorptive or *active* sites in materials such as silica gel and alumina result mainly from defects (cracks, edges etc.) where the electrostatic forces which hold the crystal lattices together are partly directed outward. It is the interaction between these forces and electrical forces within solute molecules that brings about adsorption. The greater the charge separation in the solute molecules (i.e. the greater the polarity), the greater will be the adsorptive force. For practical purposes liquid/solid chromatography is best suited to the separation of substances of medium or low polarity.

In any chromatographic adsorption system we have three interdependent variables to take into account. These are the adsorbent, the solvent, and the substances being chromatographed. Separations on adsorbents depend upon the fact that an equilibrium is set up between the molecules adsorbed on the stationary phase and those free in the moving solvent, individual molecules moving between the two phases. If the molecules of a particular component have a high affinity for the adsorbent, that component will move only slowly, while another component having less affinity will move more rapidly. The aim of the chromatographer is to choose the appropriate adsorbent and solvent system to give the best separation for a particular mixture.

The general rule in this matter is to match the polarity of the solvent with that of the sample and, in most cases, to use the more powerful (active) adsorbents for non-polar substances, and the less active adsorbents for the more polar substances.

The reason for the first rule is fairly obvious. If, for example, we chose a polar solvent for a mixture of non-polar substances, the solvent molecules would be preferentially absorbed and the sample would move rapidly through the system without a separation being achieved. Alternatively, if a non-polar solvent was used with a polar mixture, the mixture would remain at the origin and again no worthwhile separation would result.

To enable a suitable choice to be made, lists have been prepared of the commoner solvents and adsorbents in order of increasing polarity (eluting power) and activity respectively. These are based on actual practical experience and are given in Table 1.

TABLE 1

Adsorbents in order of increasing adsorptive power	Solvents in order of increasing eluting power
Sugar, starch	Hexane, petroleum ethers
Inulin	Heptane
Talc	Cyclohexane
Sodium carbonate	Carbon tetrachloride
Potassium carbonate	Benzene
Calcium carbonate	Toluene
Magnesia	Chloroform
Activated silica gel	Diethyl ether
Activated alumina	Ethyl acetate
	Pyridine
	Acetone
	Propanol
	Ethanol
	Methanol
	Water
	Mixtures of acids, bases with water, alchols or pyridine

Although these lists are very helpful a certain amount of care should be exercised, particularly with the solvents, since it is not unusual to find inversions between two particular solvents under some conditions.

Virtually any liquid can be used as a solvent in liquid/solid chromatography, and mixtures of two, three, or even four liquids of different polarities could be combined. Thus the number of solvents available to the analyst is very much greater than the number of useful adsorbents.

In practice, only about two adsorbents, silica gel and alumina, are in common use, and separations are achieved by altering the solvents or by varying the adsorptive power of the adsorbent, usually by the controlled addition of water.

The most *active* form of the adsorbent is produced by removing all the water and any organic contaminants by heating strongly. The lesser activity grades can then be produced by adding known amounts of water. This process is known as *deactivation*. The extent to which the activity has been reduced is often measured on the *Brockmann* scale. In the case of alumina, for example, the most active grade is called Brockmann activity grade I. Lower activity grades contain the following amounts of water:

Activity grade	I	II	III	IV	V
Weight of water (%)	0	3	6	10	15

The activity grade can easily be determined for the solid adsorbents, but when they have been made up into thin layers this is not quite so easy. Special dye mixtures are available to run on thin layers, the mobility of the individual dyes giving a guide to the activity.

For best results the sizes of the adsorbent particles should be within a fairly narrow range. Generally much finer particles are used in thin layer chromatography than in column chromatography. Specially prepared grades to suit the needs of the various types of chromatography are available commercially.

It should always be borne in mind that the adsorbents, with their very high surface areas, often act as efficient catalysts and can in some circumstances bring about quite important chemical changes in the components of a mixture during a separation.

The *sample load* in adsorption chromatography is very important since the adsorptive power of the surface often falls off quite markedly with increasing load, because the most active sites are occupied first. The result is that the zones of the separating components *tail* in the direction of the origin. For best results it is desirable to have the adsorbent/sample ratio as large as possible.

In normal thin layer adsorption chromatography this ratio is in the order of 1 000:1 which is quite satisfactory. The ratio in preparative thin layer or column chromatography can fall to 100:1 or even 10:1, with the result that much poorer separations are achieved.

One reason for the success of silica gel is that it has a very high capacity (the ability to separate a large quantity of mixture).

Gas/solid chromatography

Gas adsorption chromatography is used mainly for the separation of gases, and most of the media used have only limited scope. Some, such as porous silica beads, have wider applications.

The *Porasil* range of spherical porous silica beads, for example, has many advantages over the commonly used inorganic supports. The strong rigid structure of the beads and their chemical inertness allow them to be used without liquid coatings. It is also possible to produce beads with varying porosities and surface areas. In the *Porasil* range, six types are available with pore sizes ranging from 10 nm (surface area 480 m²/g) to 150 nm (surface area 1.5 m²/g).

Because the retention of volatile substances decreases with decreasing surface area, substances ranging from gases to high boiling point liquids can be separated by picking the appropriate type. Some typical separations are shown in Plate 7.

By coating the beads with a small amount of liquid phase, it is possible to combine the separation capabilities of adsorption and partition.

2.4 Ion-exchange chromatography

Ion-exchange separations are carried out with special materials with an insoluble, porous structure containing reactive groups which have associated with them labile ions which are capable of exchanging with ions in the surrounding medium. No major physical change occurs in the material during this process which invariably takes place in liquid (usually aqueous) solution.

As its name suggests, ion exchange chromatography is used for the separation of ionic substances which range from simple inorganic and organic ions to *polyelectrolytes* such as enzymes, proteins, hormones, viruses, nucleic acids and other biologically important substances.

Three types of ion-exchange materials are commonly encountered: ion-exchange *resins*, ion-exchange *gels* and ion-exchange *celluloses*. The difference between these lies partly in the nature of the exchanging groups which are incorporated into each, but mostly in the individual microstructures that each has. These differences are summarised in Fig. 5, which is reproduced by kind permission of H. Reeve Angel and Company Ltd.

It can be seen from this Figure that the pore size of the resins is much smaller than that of the other types, and for this reason the resins are mainly used for the fractionation of substances with relatively small molecules such as inorganic ions and amino acids. The larger pore sizes of the ion-exchange gels and celluloses make them particularly suitable for the fractionation of polyelectrolytes.

The initial interest in the phenomenon of ion-exchange was principally in the sphere of water softening. It was found that certain minerals, notably complicated silicates known as *zeolites*, had the capacity to remove unwanted calcium and magnesium ions from hard water and replace them with sodium ions. The zeolites thus acted as *cation-exchangers*. The uses of the zeolites, however, were very limited, since they were relatively unstable to pH changes and quantitative recovery of adsorbed material was rarely possible. From a chromatographic point of view, most of these difficulties were overcome by the introduction of synthetic ion-exchange resins.

Synthetic ion-exchange resins

The first resins were prepared by the condensation of phenol sulphonic acid with formaldehyde. The product contained reactive groups such as —OH and —COOH in addition to the more important —SO$_3$H exchange groups. Although many extremely difficult chromatographic separations of radioactive isotopes, rare earth elements and amino acids could be achieved with these, experience showed that even better and more reproducible results could be obtained with resins having only one reactive type

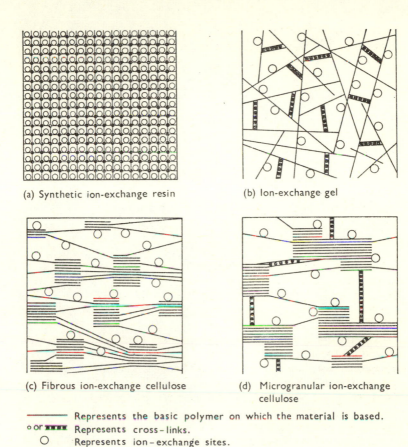

(a) Synthetic ion-exchange resin

(b) Ion-exchange gel

(c) Fibrous ion-exchange cellulose

(d) Microgranular ion-exchange cellulose

——————— Represents the basic polymer on which the material is based.
○ or ▪▪▪▪ Represents cross–links.
○   Represents ion–exchange sites.

FIG. 5. A diagrammatic comparison of the micro structures of four different types of ion-exchange media

of grouping. Most of the modern polystyrene-based resins are of this type. Modern production techniques have also led to resins with more uniform pore size.

The polystyrene-based resins are made by polymerising together a mixture of styrene and a cross-linking agent such as divinylbenzene, and then reacting the product with a suitable reagent to introduce reactive groups. By suitable choice of reagent one can introduce strongly or weakly acidic groups (*cation exchangers*), or strongly or weakly basic groups (*anion exchangers*). Two examples are shown in Fig.6.

The example shown in Fig. 6(a) is a strong cation-exchange resin, because the nuclear sulphonic acid grouping —SO_3H confers strongly acidic properties to the resin. Hydrogen ions (H^+) are the ones capable of exchange in this case. Similarly, in the example shown in Fig. 6 (b), the resin matrix contains a substituted ammonium hydroxide grouping —$[N(CH_3)_3]^+OH^-$, hydroxyl ions (OH^-) being those capable of exchange.

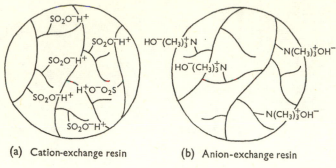

(a) Cation-exchange resin   (b) Anion-exchange resin

Fig. 6

The reaction between the cation-exchange resin R—H$^+$ and sodium ions would be

$$R—H^+ + Na^+ \rightleftharpoons R—Na^+ + H^+$$

while that of the anion-exchange resin with chloride ions would be

$$R—OH^- + Cl^- \rightleftharpoons R—Cl^- + OH^-$$

Because virtually any ion of the appropriate kind can be exchanged, the *counter-ion* on the resin can be in any form. For practical purposes, however, it is usual for cation-exchangers to be used in the hydrogen (H$^+$) or sodium (Na$^+$) form, and anion-exchangers in the chloride (Cl$^-$) or hydroxide (OH$^-$) forms. To convert one form into another, the resin is washed with a large excess of a strong solution containing the appropriate ion, which drives the equilibrium in the desired direction. Thus to convert a resin from the sodium to the hydrogen form, one would simply wash with an excess of strong acid.

In ion-exchange column chromatography, a solution containing the ions to be separated is introduced at the top of the column. The conditions are usually chosen so that ions in the solution are rapidly exchanged with those of the resin, and one thus gets a narrow band of the sample ions at the top. Different ions are then displaced one by one, either by slowly changing the pH of the eluting liquid, or by increasing the concentration or type of ions in the eluting liquid, or by increasing the temperature.

In the separation of the cations of the rare earth elements, for example, the sample is introduced onto a column of cation-exchange resin under conditions which allow the ions to be adsorbed at the top of the column. The individual cations are then selectivley desorbed with sodium citrate solution, the heavier cations being displaced first because they form the strongest complexes with the citrate ions.

Normally ion-exchange separations are carried out in aqueous solutions but, provided ions are present, there is no reason why this process should not be carried out in non-aqueous solvents.

Ion-exchange gels

By introducing the appropriate exchanging groups into the matrix of the gels used for gel filtration, it is possible to produce media which are particularly valuable for the separation of polyelectrolytes. It is now possible to obtain Sephadex ion-exchange gels with weakly basic, weakly acidic, strongly basic and strongly acidic groups.

Ion-exchange celluloses

In many ways the ion-exchange celluloses resemble the above group, in that they are both derived from carbohydrate polymers, often contain similar exchanging groups, and are used for similar fractionations. The main differences lie at the macro, micro and molecular levels.

Whereas the gels are in the form of spherical beads with a more or less uniform 3-dimensional network of cross-linked dextran chains, the celluloses are fibrous and have the irregular structure of native cellulose. This can be seen by reference to Fig. 5 and Plate 1.

As a result of much research carried out by manufacturers, new improved *fibrous* products (Plate 1b) and *microgranular* products (Plate 1c) have been introduced. The improvement in resolution which these give over an older product can be clearly seen from Plate 2.

The fibrous exchangers are chosen for column chromatography when a good flowrate is the prime consideration. The microgranular form is chosen when good resolution is required.

3 Paper Chromatography

Partition chromatography on sheets or strips of filter paper is one of the simplest and most widely used of the chromatographic techniques. A variety of specially prepared grades of paper is available to suit particular needs, but as a general rule Whatman No. 1 or Whatman No. 3 filter papers are used for analytical work and Whatman No. 3 or Whatman 3MM for preparative work.

3.1 Samples for chromatography

Samples are applied to the paper from solution, and so solids are always dissolved in a small quantity of a suitable solvent. Pure substances can usually be applied directly, but extracts prepared from biological tissue often require preliminary purification before they can be applied. The reason for this is that large amounts of protein or salts in the extract can interfere with the partitioning process by extracting water from the solvent, and give rise to tailing on the chromatograms. Large amounts of extraneous material can also obscure the separated components.

There are several methods of removing unwanted substances; lipids can be extracted with organic solvents, proteins can be precipitated with alchol and salts can be removed by treatment with ion-exchange resins or by an electrolytic method.

Preliminary fractionation of biological extracts on small columns of an ion-exchange resin is often very valuable. By a suitable choice of the resin type and conditions of chromatography, non-ionic substances can be separated from ionic substances, and the latter can be further fractionated. In this way it is often possible to obtain samples containing only one or two molecular types.

Another method of removing salts is by electrolysis and a number of devices, differing slightly in principle and design, is available. We can perhaps illustrate the principle by reference to the BTL apparatus shown in Plate 10. This apparatus has a three-part desalting cell, a cathode compartment containing dilute sulphuric acid, a central compartment in which the sample is placed, and an anode compartment containing dilute sodium hydroxide solution. The compartments are separated by special ion exchange membranes which allow ions to pass in one direction only.

On passing a current, the cations and anions in the sample selectively pass through the membranes into the appropriate compartments, thereby diminishing the concentration of electrolytes in the centre compartment. The progress of desalting is followed on the milliammeter on the front of the unit.

3.2 Application of the sample to paper

Having selected the size and grade of paper to be used, a pencil line is drawn parallel to one edge and at a suitable distance from it. A number of small crosses are marked on the line (equal distances apart) corresponding to the number of samples to be applied and the nature of each sample written on in pencil. The paper is then placed on a bench with the baseline overhanging slightly.

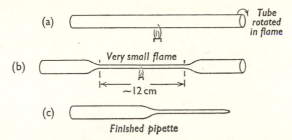

FIG. 7. Construction of a micropipette for streaking

A drop of each sample is spotted on to the appropriate position with a short length of cappilary tubing or a platinum loop. Platinum loops have the advantage that they can be used over and over again if they are washed and heated strongly in a bunsen flame after each application. Glass capillary tubes are best discarded after use. The spots should be about 5 mm

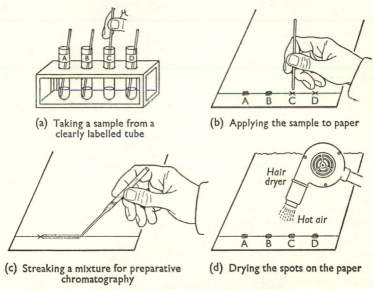

(a) Taking a sample from a clearly labelled tube

(b) Applying the sample to paper

(c) Streaking a mixture for preparative chromatography

(d) Drying the spots on the paper

FIG. 8. Application of samples to paper

in diameter. Larger spots lead to poorer separations. Drawing out spotting tubes to a fine point greatly helps in getting small spots. If more test substance is required than is present in one drop (for example when the solution is dilute) the spot is allowed to dry and a similar application made. Drying is made more rapid by the use of a hair dryer.

For preparative paper chromatography, streaks of the sample are applied, rather than single spots.

When the spots are dry the paper is ready for *development* which is the name given to the process in which a solvent flows through the paper to produce a separation. It is at this stage that the paper is folded or coiled where necessary in preparation for the next step.

3.3 Choice of solvent

The solvent for development obviously depends upon the nature of the substances to be separated, and a knowledge of which solvent to try comes mainly by experience. Solvent systems have been devised for separating the members of almost any class of compounds.

Chromatographic solvents for paper partition chromatography can be made by simply saturating an organic solvent such as *n*-butanol with water. Many popular solvents are of this type, but several useful partitioning liquids only incorporate a small amount of water so that polar compounds (amino acids, sugars and phenolic compounds) move very slowly or fail to separate in such binary systems.

To overcome this, another component (or components) is often added to the mixture. These may be either acids, bases or complexing agents, and typical examples include acetic and formic acids, pyridine and ammonia solution, and hydrochloric acid solution. They serve two functions. They allow more water to be incorporated in the solvent whilst improving the solubility of some substances or depressing that of others. *Ternary* (three component) solvents are very widely used. The type of solvent commonly encountered will be found in chapter eight.

The formulation of solvents used to be such that when the components were mixed together, two layers resulted. The organic layer could then be removed and used for development. The advantage of this was that it ensured that the solvent was saturated with water, but it wasted material and was also time-consuming. The modern practice is to make up one-phase solvents which correspond in composition to the organic layers described above. When making up these solvents it is essential to use exactly the quantities specified and to shake well before use.

There is little doubt that adsorption effects play an important part in some separations. It is possible, for example, to achieve good separations using a single solvent such as water for developing the paper.

Development can be carried out either by allowing the solvent to travel up the paper (the *ascending* technique) or down the paper (the *descending* technique). Apparatus for the two techniques is shown in Plate 9.

3.4 The descending technique

The developing solvent is placed in a trough made of an inert material (e.g. glass) which is set in the chromatography tank as shown in Fig. 9(*a*).

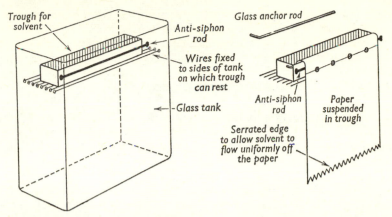

FIG. 9(a). Layout of the tank for descending chromatography

FIG. 9(b). Insertion of paper

Some of the solvent is poured into the bottom of the tank so as to saturate the atmosphere with its vapour. The paper, prepared as described in 3.2, is then suspended in the solvent and the lid placed securely on the tank. (The paper is anchored in the trough by means of a glass rod and passes over a second rod slightly higher than the edge of the trough to prevent siphoning of the solvent.)

3.5 The ascending technique

In this technique, solvent is placed in the bottom of the tank and the paper suspended in it by some device placed in the tank (Fig. 10(a), (b), (c)).

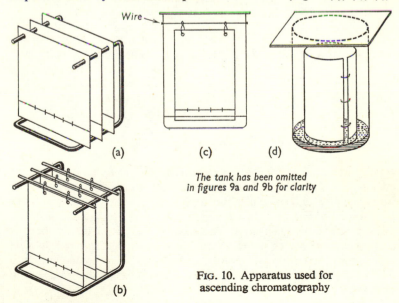

The tank has been omitted in figures 9a and 9b for clarity

FIG. 10. Apparatus used for ascending chromatography

Alternatively, the paper can be curled into a cylinder, the two ends clipped together (Fig. 10(*d*)), and the paper dipped into solvent in the bottom of the tank. In each case the tank is securely closed with a lid.

3.6 Choice of descending or ascending technique

For many separations a choice between these two techniques is one of personal preference, as similar results can be obtained with either. There are, however, differences which recommend one or the other for certain applications.

With the ascending technique, assuming that the atmosphere in the tank is saturated with the vapour of the developing solvent, the solvent can ascend only until it reaches the top edge of the paper, when the flow ceases. Thus, all the compounds remain on the paper and the distance travelled by the solvent is fixed. This is of particular value for two-dimensional separations. The ascending method also usually gives better results with very volatile solvents. A disadvantage of this technique is that compounds with low R_f values are often incompletely separated. With the descending technique the developing solvent can be allowed to run off the end of the paper under the influence of gravity so that one is able to increase considerably the effective length of the run and thus improve the separation.

It is important, therefore, that students should familiarise themselves with both methods.

3.7 Drying the paper

When the solvent has travelled the required distance, or for the required time, the paper or papers are removed from the tank and the position of the solvent front noted by tearing the paper slightly at the edges. Drying is carried out in a fume cupboard by means of a fan or electric hair dryer. The paper is then ready for location of the compounds.

3.8 Location of substances on paper chromatograms

Having attempted a separation, we naturally wish to locate the separated compounds. If they are coloured, this presents little or no difficulty, but many compounds, particularly those of biological interest, are colourless and hence invisible. Several methods are available for use in this case. Physical methods, which utilise particular properties of the compounds such as fluorescence or radioactivity, are popular but have only limited applicability. The most widely used method of locating compounds is to react them with a chemical reagent (or reagents) to produce a coloured product.

Physical methods

1 *Fluorescence*

A number of unsaturated organic compounds fluoresce, i.e. they have the property of absorbing ultraviolet or violet light of short (invisible) wavelength and emitting light of longer (visible) wavelength. These compounds, although invisible on chromatograms in ordinary light, can readily be detected under an ultraviolet lamp. The wavelength of the light emitted, and hence the colour one sees, is characteristic of the compound and is therefore useful for the purpose of identification.

Numerous fluorescent compounds are present in most plant tissues.

2 *Radioactivity*

The widespread use of nuclear power has made available a number of 'labelled' (radioactive) compounds for research. These can be detected on chromatograms by means of a special counter.

Physical methods of location have the advantage over chemical methods that the substances on the chromatogram are not converted into other compounds, and so they can be removed and studied further.

In the majority of cases a physical method cannot be used and therefore the separated compounds are located by a chemical technique.

Chemical methods

Colourless compounds on the paper are converted to coloured products by treatment with a *location reagent*. The location reagent can be simply a gas as in the case of hydrogen sulphide (for the location of metallic ions which form coloured sulphides), but the vast majority are solids or liquids, which are applied to the chromatogram in solution. Common solvents for the reagents include water, methyl, ethyl and *n*-butyl alcohols and acetone. The location process can be one stage or involve several stages. In the latter case it is often advisable to allow chromatograms to dry, at least partially, after each stage before proceding with the next. Sometimes heat is necessary to complete a reaction.

Solutions of reagents can be applied by dipping the paper into a solution of the reagent or by spraying the solution on to the paper.

The dipping technique

All that is required is a shallow tray made of an inert material and of such dimensions that a chromatogram can be drawn through a solution of a locating reagent without touching the sides. This is demonstrated in Fig. 11.

Good separations can be spoilt by the use of the wrong solvent for the location reagent or by careless application. It is essential that the compounds and their coloured reaction products are almost insoluble in the solvent chosen, otherwise diffuse spots or complete solution of the spots will occur. Acetone, when it satisfies these conditions, is a particularly useful solvent to use for dipping because it rapidly evaporates from the chromatogram, allowing any further stages to proceed almost immediately. If the chromatogram is to be stored, perhaps for future comparison with other chromatograms, a final dip is often introduced to remove any excess locating reagent from the paper.

These points can best be illustrated by considering two actual dipping procedures:

(1) The most widely used reagent for detecting amino acids (the 'building blocks' of proteins) is ninhydrin. Ninhydrin is a white solid which is applied to the paper as a 0.1 to 0.25 per cent solution in a suitable solvent. The reaction with amino acids can be represented simply:

$$\underset{\text{(colourless)}}{\text{amino acid}} + \underset{\text{(colourless)}}{\text{ninhydrin}} \xrightarrow{\text{heat}} \underset{\text{(blue-lilac)}}{\text{coloured product}}$$

Experience has shown that for dipping, acetone is better than other solvents for ninhydrin since the colour is produced more rapidly and is more intense. The paper is dipped into the acetone solution, removed, and after allowing the acetone to evaporate the paper is heated at about 100°C for 5–10 minutes to allow the colour to develop.

(2) A popular and sensitive method of detecting reducing substances, of which glucose and maltose (malt sugar) are examples, on paper chromatograms, is to dip the dry chromatogram into silver nitrate solution

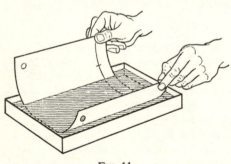

Fig. 11

(1 volume of 10 per cent aqueous silver nitrate diluted with 100 volumes of acetone) and then to take the paper out and allow the acetone to evaporate off. No reaction takes place in this first stage and the paper remains blank. On making alkaline by dipping into 0.5 N NaOH in ethyl alcohol containing a little water, the silver nitrate is reduced at the spots containing the reducing sugars and metallic silver is deposited. One thus gets a chromatogram with discrete brown spots indicating the position of the sugars. The excess silver nitrate left would rapidly darken in contact with the air and has therefore to be removed by a third dip in 5 per cent sodium thiosulphate solution if the chromatogram is to be stored.

The dipping technique cannot be used if either the compounds on the chromatogram or their coloured reaction products are soluble in the solvent used for the locating reagent, and in this case spraying is recommended.

The spraying technique

A solution of the locating reagent is sprayed uniformly over the surface of the chromatogram by means of an atomiser, such as a scent spray or special chromatographic spray bottle, operated by hand bellows or a stream of compressed air. The spraying technique is shown in Fig. 12.

If two or more locating reagents are used, they are simply applied one after the other. Drying the paper after each application is less important with the spraying technique. Excess locating reagent is usually removed if chromatograms are to be stored.

In a multistage location procedure, some reagents can be applied by dipping, others by spraying, according to personal preference.

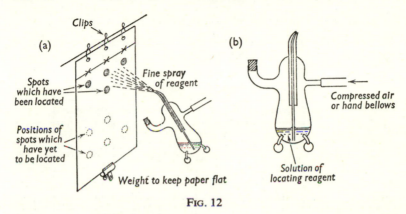

FIG. 12

3.9 Limits of detection on chromatograms

One of the major advantages of paper chromatography is the sensitivity with which compounds can be located after separation. Amounts as little as 0.1 microgram (1 microgram is one-millionth of a gram) of some compounds can be detected with routine reagents. The lower limit for the detection of most compounds is between 1–50 μg.

This extreme sensitivity is one of the most important features of paper (as well as other forms) of chromatography. Many naturally occuring organic compounds can only be isolated in quantities of the order of a few milligrams, but even with such minute amounts many reactions can be carried out and the products separated and identified. Paper chromatography has thus played a very important part in elucidating the chemistry of such compounds.

3.10 The concept of R values

It was mentioned in the previous chapter that the movement of any substance relative to the solvent front in a given chromatographic system is constant and characteristic of that substance. In paper chromatography the R_f value is constantly quoted. This is defined as

$$R_f = \frac{\text{Distance moved by the substance}}{\text{Distance moved by the solvent front}}$$

In some cases, the solvent front is run off the end of the paper and it is more convenient to express the movement of any substance by comparing it with the movement of another substance (which is nearly always chemically similar). R_X values, rather than R_f values, are more valuable here.

$$R_X = \frac{\text{Distance moved by the substance}}{\text{Distance moved by the standard substance X}}$$

In the field of sugars, for example, movements are often quoted relative to glucose and R_G values used. These points are summarised in Fig. 13.

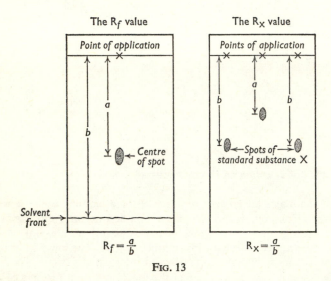

Fig. 13

3.11 Two-dimensional paper chromatography

The separation of a complex mixture of substances can often be effected satisfactorily by chromatography in one direction only, but in some cases the mixture is so complicated that one-directional chromatography brings about only a partial separation. In this case, chromatography using another solvent at right angles to the first can be used to obtain a better separation of the spots.

A square sheet of filter paper is used. The test solution is applied near one corner of the paper (Fig. 8) and ascending or descending chromatography carried out.

The paper is removed from the tank, dried, and turned through 90°, and the chromatogram developed in a different solvent. This technique allows the path of migration to be increased and also enables the partially separated components to be further separated in a solvent with characteristics different from those of the first. After the second development the

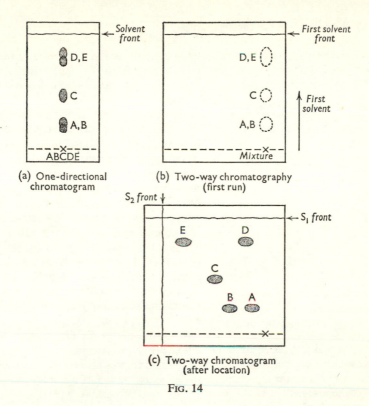

(a) One-directional chromatogram

(b) Two-way chromatography (first run)

(c) Two-way chromatogram (after location)

FIG. 14

paper is removed from the tank. It is then dried and the substances located with a selective reagent.

A given compound on a two-dimensional chromatogram can be identified by comparison of its position with that of a standard compound (either on the same chromatogram or one similarly prepared).

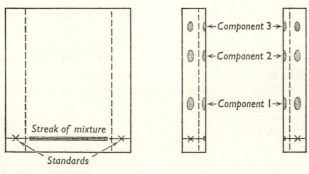

FIG. 15(a). Preparation of the paper

FIG. 15(b). Sprayed marginal strips

3.12 Preparative paper chromatography

Preparative paper chromatography is carried out on thick filter paper. The separated components can be removed from the paper with suitable solvents, the solutions concentrated, and the compounds crystallised.

The solution containing the mixture is applied as a streak to the base line of the paper as shown in Fig. 15(a). A solution of standard compounds is applied close to the two vertical edges of the paper. The paper is developed in the chosen solvent, removed after a sufficient length of time, and dried. Marginal strips are then cut from the paper so as to include the standard compounds and part of the mixture. These are sprayed or dipped in a locating reagent (if the compounds on the filter paper are not naturally coloured), thereby showing the positions of the bands containing the components in the mixture (Fig. 15(b)). By fitting the marginal strips back on to the filter paper, the

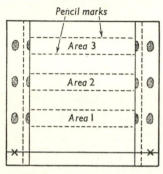

FIG. 16. Mapping the areas

areas containing the separated components can be mapped out in pencil. These areas are cut out with scissors and each cut into strips. The strips from each area are then clipped together (by means of a staple) and the substances eluted from them with a suitable solvent. A typical arrangement for this is shown in Fig. 17.

3.13 Quantitative paper chromatography

Sometimes it is required to make a quantitative measurement of a particular component in a mixture in addition to the usual qualitative ones. This can be achieved in several ways.

One simple method, which is basically the same as described for preparative work, consists of applying a suitable and accurately measured volume of the mixture to a spot on the baseline of the paper by means of a calibrated capillary tube or micro-pipette. Samples of the component to be measured are also applied on the same paper.

The paper is developed, dried, and the marginal strips cut out and treated with a suitable reagent (Fig. 18).

The appropriate strip is cut out and the sample eluted off the paper with a suitable solvent. The compounds so eluted can then be determined by one of the multitude of methods available for substances in solution (colour reactions, titration, micro-gravimetric procedures, etc.).

For the success of this and other quantitative methods it is obvious that the separation itself must be complete or other compounds will interfere.

Measurements on paper

If a reagent is available which will react with the component to produce a colour, the intensity of which is proportional to the amount of that component present, then quantitative measurements can be made directly on the paper. Such methods are always *comparative* in nature.

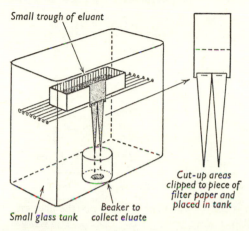

FIG. 17. Elution of the substance from strips of the filter paper obtained from each separate area

An accurately measured volume of the mixture is applied to a spot on the baseline as in the previous method. Accurately known amounts of the component being studied are then applied to a further series of spots at each side of the unknown. After allowing the spots to dry, the paper is developed, dried, and the compounds located under carefully controlled conditions.

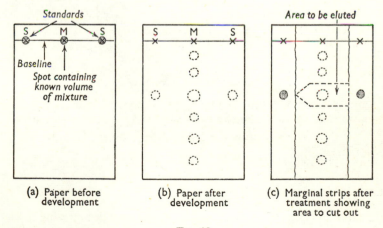

(a) Paper before development

(b) Paper after development

(c) Marginal strips after treatment showing area to cut out

FIG. 18

To make a rough estimation of the amount present in the unknown, a simple visual comparison is all that is required. The range of standards applied to the paper should include the amount present in the unknown to aid the comparison. For many purposes rough estimations of this type are quite satisfactory, but for more accurate work the intensity of each spot is measured with a photoelectric device known as a *Photodensitometer*.

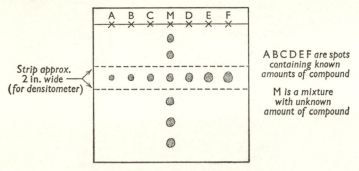

Strip approx. 2 in. wide (for densitometer)

ABCDEF are spots containing known amounts of compound

M is a mixture with unknown amount of compound

FIG. 19. Chromatogram after location

A thin strip is cut from the chromatogram (the area enclosed by dotted lines in Fig. 19), placed between two sheets of glass, and then into the holder of the densitometer. The machine is set to zero on a section of the strip free from any compound, and the strip is then moved in small stages past the beam and the deflection on the dial recorded. A graph of dial deflection against distance down the paper is then plotted. The area under each curve is proportional to the amount of compound in that spot. This method will give determinations accurate to within 5 per cent in most cases.

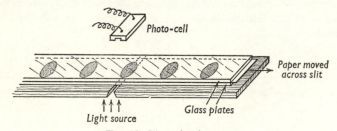

Photo-cell

Paper moved across slit

Light source

Glass plates

FIG. 20. Photodensitometer

Other methods of determining the quantity in an unknown spot include comparison of the spot area with that of known spots, using the equation:

$$\text{area of spot} \propto \log (\text{concentration}),$$

and specific methods like measurement of radioactivity.

3.14 Ion-exchange papers

The versatility of paper chromatography can be extended by using special cellulose derivatives (with groups capable of exchanging ions) to fabricate the paper instead of the usual cellulose, thus making it possible to carry out ion-exchange separations. Such derivatives include carboxymethyl cellulose and cellulose citrate and phosphate (exchange ions of the type X^+), and aminoethyl and diethylaminoethyl cellulose (exchange ions of the type Y^-).

The procedure with these materials is similar to that with ordinary paper, but there are one or two differences. The papers come in a particular form (acid papers, for example, being in the form of their ammonium or sodium salts) and may need some modification before use (i.e. to convert them to the hydrogen form). Apart from this precaution, the use of these papers is very simple. Less trouble has to be taken when applying the sample, and separations can be achieved with better resolution than with ordinary papers.

Development of ion-exchange papers can be carried out with a solution containing ions to displace those of the substances being separated (i.e. by ion-exchange). Alternatively, an ion-free solvent can be employed, and separations are then similar to those on ordinary filter paper, i.e. by partition. This is particularly valuable for two-dimensional separations.

Ion-exchange separations can also be performed on papers which have been impregnated with ion-exchange resins.

3.15 Reverse-phase chromatography

Substances which are only very sparingly soluble in water are not separated by ordinary paper chromatographic methods as they move with the solvent front. The technique can be extended to compounds of this type by drying the paper and impregnating it with olive oil, silicone oil, paraffin or rubber latex.

The impregnated paper absorbs the organic component of the solvent and it is partition between this and the solvent which brings about a separation. This is referred to as *reverse-phase* paper chromatography. In some instances, the impregnating material itself acts as the stationary phase.

The solvents for reverse-phase separations usually consist of an organic liquid containing a little water.

3.16 Electrophoresis

Electrophoresis is a technique which is closely associated with chromatography and is often used in conjunction with it. Separations depend upon differences in the electrical properties of the components in a mixture, so that often substances which would be difficult to separate by chromatographic methods are very readily separated by this technique (and vice versa).

Electrophoresis is an incomplete form of electrolysis in which the charged particles are stopped somewhere along their paths to the electrodes. There are two types: (a) Free electrophoresis, in which the separated substances are in solution, and are therefore free to diffuse the moment the current is switched off, (b) Zone electrophoresis, in which the separation is carried out on a supporting medium, such as starch gel or strips of filter paper. It is the latter kind in which we are interested here.

A pencil line is drawn perpendicular to the length of the paper, and spots of samples applied to positions marked on the line. As there is no solvent front with which to compare the movement of each substance, the movement is usually compared with a standard compound which is therefore also applied to the baseline. The paper is carefully moistened with a buffer solution suitable to effect separation, and the two ends dipped into pots of the same buffer solution in an arrangement like the one shown in Fig. 21(*a*).

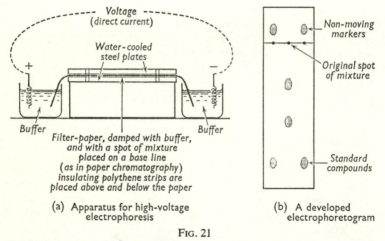

(a) Apparatus for high-voltage electrophoresis

(b) A developed electrophoretogram

Fig. 21

When the current is passed, the supporting medium acts as a 'bridge' between the two pots of buffer solution, and any substance in the mixture which bears an electrical charge will migrate (the direction being governed by the nature of the charge). In many cases, molecules which bear no electrical charge can have an electrophoretic mobility since they form complex ions with ions present in the buffer solution; many sugar molecules can be separated in this way.

After a suitable time, the current is switched off and the paper removed from the apparatus. After allowing the paper to dry, the separated components can be located with a locating reagent if they are not naturally coloured, in the same way as described for paper chromatograms.

The rate of migration of a substance during electrophoresis depends upon several factors, e.g. the voltage applied, the structure of the ion, and so on.

It is necessary to put on the filter paper a non-moving 'marker', i.e. a compound which will have no electrophoretic mobility, since there is a tendency for substances to move in a direction opposite to that of their electrophoretic movement, by electro-osmosis (see textbook of Physical Chemistry). The distance of migration of a substance during electrophoresis is quoted as its M_X value, where this is the distance migrated by the compound in question from the non-moving marker divided by the distance migrated by a standard compound X from the non-moving marker.

The electrophoretic mobility of a compound in a mixture is independent of the other substances present.

In many cases, the separation of the components in a mixture can be carried out by using chromatography in one direction coupled with electrophoresis at right angles (cf. two-way paper chromatography).

The scope of paper electrophoresis can be extended by the use of cellulose acetate strips. These are more or less transparent and have a much more uniform structure and smaller pore size than ordinary filter paper, allowing much better resolution. This feature, coupled with the ability of cellulose acetate to separate small amounts of material, makes this a particularly valuable technique in clinical diagnosis involving serum proteins, haemoglobins, etc. and for evaluating body fluids such as cerebro-spinal fluid, urine and tears.

A small selection of the kind of apparatus used for electrophoresis with paper and cellulose acetate strips or thin layer plates is shown in Plates 12 and 13.

4 Thin Layer Chromatography

Paper chromatography is a versatile technique, but its use is limited by the fact that separations can be conducted only with fibrous materials such as cellulose, since other valuable media such as silica gel, alumina and gel filtration beads cannot be made into sheets. This difficulty can be overcome by supporting thin layers of these substances on an appropriate base. The usual method is to support them on glass plates, in which case the product is referred to as a *chromatoplate*. Thin layers supported on solvent-resistant plastic sheets (*chromatosheets*) are also available commercially.

Two types of layer are useful: *solid layers* which adhere to the support by virtue of the adherent qualities of the material itself or because of a binding agent incorporated with it, and *loose layers*. The latter are only really used for determining the activity of adsorbents and in one or two special applications.

Thin layer separations resemble those on paper in some ways, but the much wider choice of media means that separations by partition, adsorption, gel filtration and ion-exchange can be performed by this technique. The particular properties of thin layers also allow much shorter development times to be achieved. It is not uncommon, for example, for excellent separations to be obtained with thin layers in 20–40 minutes. Even separations on cellulose thin layers can be completed in a fraction of the time that would have been taken by paper chromatography. One reason for this is the fine particle size of most thin layer media, which gives improved resolution and compact spots.

The speed and versatility of thin layer chromatography makes it ideal for teaching purposes.

4.1 Preparation of chromatoplates

(a) Solid layers

Solid layers are prepared by applying a slurry of the chosen medium in a suitable liquid on to clean glass plates. Cleaning of plates is best conducted by storing them in a strong solution of washing soda, and rinsing thoroughly with water before use.

It is essential for optimum results to ensure that the layer is uniform. The particle size, surface structure and adhesiveness of the medium must be quite carefully controlled if reproducible results are to be obtained. These requirements are best met by commerically produced and standard-ised products. It should be stressed, however, that even some of these contain a certain amount of unwanted organic material on occasion, which can obscure separations or contaminate substances isolated from the plates.

If the material adheres badly, a binding agent such as calcium sulphate is often incorporated in small quantities. Other additives to thin layer media include special fluorescing agents which allow spots on the developed chromatograms to be seen under ultraviolet light.

It used to be common practice to incorporate a binding agent into nearly all the media intended for thin layer work. The experiments described in the back of the book, in fact, involve binder-containing silica gel. Modern products, however, have greatly improved adhesive properties and in most cases a binder is either superfluous or even undesirable. If a binder is not incorporated, slurries of the material can be stored in stoppered bottles almost indefinitely.

Slurries are normally made in water, which may contain acids, bases, buffers or complexing agents if they are required. The major problem in thin layer work is to get the right consistency. If the slurry is too thin, it will run too quickly and produce excessively thin layers whereas, if it is too thick, spreading is difficult and one can easily get lines along the plates or clumping. The manufacturer's instructions should therefore be followed carefully.

The authors have found the following method useful for preparing slurries of *binder-free* silica gel and cellulose. A suitable amount of the dry powder is placed in a mortar and distilled water is added slowly with grinding until a thick cream is obtained. More water is added until the slurry flows cleanly down the walls of the vessel. It is then ready for use. As the aim of this procedure is to eliminate lumps before spreading, even better results are obtained if the slurry is prepared in an homogeniser.

Spreading of thin layers can be performed in a variety of ways. The simplest method is to stick strips of adhesive tape on oppostite sides of a plate, and to spread the slurry by rolling a glass rod along the tape. Alternatively, a simple device, made by pushing short lengths of rubber or plastic tubing on the ends of a glass rod in a 'wheel and axle' arrangment, can be rolled along to produce the layers. By altering the thickness of the adhesive tape or the tubing, layers of any desired thickness can be produced.

By far the best results, however, can be obtained with one of the commercially produced spreaders, one example of which is shown in Fig. 22(*a*). In this particular design, glass plates of identical thickness are arranged in a row on a template and coated in one continuous operation by means of the special spreader shown in Fig. 22(*b*). This particular principle requires the use of high precision plates which are very expensive, and most other spreaders have been designed to allow much cheaper plates to be used. A number of the features of these spreaders is shown in Plates 15, 16 and 17.

There are basically two alternative methods for doing this. In the Quickfit & Quartz model and the Shandon models, the plates are pressed either upward or downward by means of compressed air or lever action against a guide rail. This ensures that the surfaces of all the plates are in the same plane, irrespective of minor variations in plate thickness. In these models the layers are spread by moving the spreader along the plates as shown in Fig. 22(*a*).

In the alternative designs of CAMAG and BTL, shown in Plates 16 and 17, the reservoir holding the slurry remains stationary while the plates to be coated are moved underneath. Both models allow for variations in plate thickness, and both are available in manually operated or motorised versions.

It can be seen from the photographs of these models that the design of the spreaders in each case is slightly different. In some the gap setting (and hence the thickness of the layer) is fixed, while in others it can be set to personal preference. The usual thickness of layers for thin layer chromatography is 0.25 mm. Thinner layers usually give a more rapid but less effective separation. Thicker layers (0.5 or 1 mm) are used for micro-preparative work.

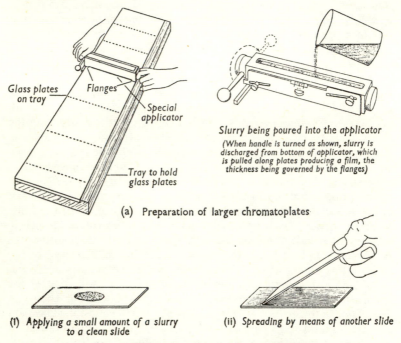

Glass plates on tray   Flanges

Special applicator

Tray to hold glass plates

Slurry being poured into the applicator
(When handle is turned as shown, slurry is discharged from bottom of applicator, which is pulled along plates producing a film, the thickness being governed by the flanges)

(a) Preparation of larger chromatoplates

(i) Applying a small amount of a slurry to a clean slide

(ii) Spreading by means of another slide

(b) Simple chromatoplates on microscope slides

FIG. 22. Preparation of chromatoplates

Normally chromatoplates are prepared in sizes ranging from 2.5 × 20 cm to 20 × 20 cm. For laboratory or class demonstration purposes smaller plates such as microscope slides are ideal. The slurry can be applied to these small plates by an extremely simple procedure like the one illustrated in Fig. 22(b) or, alternatively, the slides can be dipped into the slurry, or the slurry can be carefully sprayed onto the plates. The best results, however, are obtained with miniaturised spreaders which are specially designed for the purpose.

Having prepared the chromatoplates, the next step is to dry them in an oven at 100–105°C for about 2 hours. They are then fully activated and are suitable for adsorption chromatography. For partition chromatography on cellulose or silica gel layers, a certain amount of moisture is essential. This is achieved by leaving the dry chromatoplates exposed to the atmosphere for a time, a process referred to as deactivation. Certain media such as swollen gel filtration beads should be allowed to dry slowly since heating in the above manner would ruin their value.

(b) Loose layers

Loose layers can be prepared from the dry powdered media by whichever of the above methods is appropriate. Great care should be exercised in handling the layers, both in applying substances and in development; the latter has to be carried out with the plate in a nearly horizontal position.

4.2 Chromatosheets and ready-prepared chromatoplates

For those who do not wish to go to the trouble of preparing their own thin layer plates there are two alternatives: ready-prepared chromatoplates and pre–coated chromatosheets. Both are available with a wide range of coating materials, and the precision of coating makes good reproducibility of separations possible. Both have improved abrasion resistance so that one can write on the layer with a pencil, but they are relatively very expensive.

The chromatogram sheets are produced by precision-coating a layer of the appropriate medium on a flexible polyester (ethylene terephthalate) film. Usually a binder, polyvinyl alcohol, is incorporated, and sheets with a fluorescent indicator are also available.

4.3 Choice of medium

As mentioned previously, almost any material can be used for thin layers, and some of the factors involved in the choice have already been discussed in the introduction. The most popular media are microgranular or micro-crystalline cellulose (partition chromatography), silica gel (for partition and adsorption) and alumina (for adsorption).

4.4 Choice of solvent

The choice of solvent will, of course, depend on the nature of the substances being separated and the material on which the separation is to be carried out. A general rule in making a choice of solvent is to match the polarity of the solvent to that of the substances being separated. Thus for water-soluble substances one would choose cellulose or silica gel layers, and use one of the solvents described for paper chromatography (q.v.). For less polar substances, one would probably choose activated silica gel of alumina layers, and then select a suitable non-aqueous solvent.

A simple technique which enables a rapid choice of solvent to be made consists in placing a series of spots of the mixture at intervals on a chromatoplate. Trial solvents are then applied to the centre of each spot by means of a thin capillary and the spots allowed to migrate radially. This is shown in Fig. 23.

Solvent 2 would be the most suitable in the above example.

Because of the similarities between the separations achieved on thin layers and columns of a particular material, it is often convenient to try out a variety of solvents on thin layers before selecting the one most suitable for use on a column.

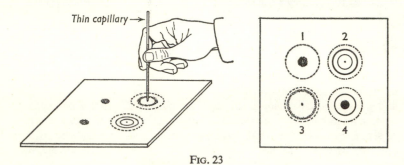

FIG. 23

4.5 Application of samples to chromatoplates

The methods are very much the same as those described for paper chromatography, except that the greater delicacy of many of the layers makes it necessary to take much more care. The use of a *spotting template* which is provided by most manufacturers greatly facilitates spotting. An example of the template is shown in Plate 15.

The samples are applied to the base line from a fine capillary and the solvent in which the substances are dissolved is allowed to evaporate. Evaporation from thin layers is quite rapid so that a hair drier or similar apparatus is usually unnecessary. Several drops can be applied to the same spot as long as the solvent is allowed to evaporate between each application. The usual amount to apply to each spot is about 1 mm³.

If the amount applied has to be accurately measured, special mm³ pipettes or precision bore capillary tubes are used.

The 'streaking pipette' for applying streaks of the sample to paper chromatograms (Figs. 6 and 7), can be used only for thin layers with high abrasion resistance. For other layers, or when it is desired to apply an accurate volume of sample to the plate, specially designed streakers are used. The CAMAG chromatocharger shown in Plate 19 is an example of this kind of device. The sample solution is contained in a microsyringe with a plunger body fitting on the top. The plunger assembly is supported on a sloping rail so that, as the device is drawn along the rail, the syringe plunger is slowly forced downward, ejecting a steady stream of liquid as it does so. It is thus possible to apply a very narrow, uniform streak along the length of the chromatoplate. By altering the slope of the rail, the

Plate 1 Chromatographic media Theoretically the ideal shape for chromatographic media is spherical like the synthetic Sephadex beads, but many valuable media such as inorganic adsorbents, diatomaceous earths and the Whatman cellulose products shown below have their own individual forms.

Whatever the source, for optimum results it is usually necessary to grade the media into fairly narrow ranges of particle sizes, the actual range being chosen to suit particular applications.

Sephadex gel filtration beads
Pharmacia Fine Chemicals

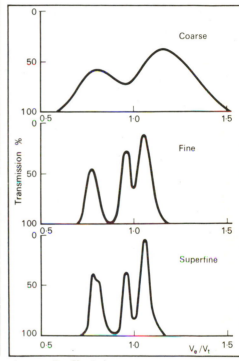

Pharmacia Fine Chemicals

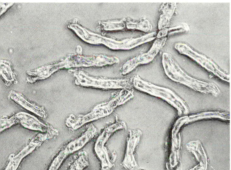

Whatman advanced fibrous ion-exchange cellulose
H Reeve Angel & Co Ltd

Whatman advanced microgranular ion-exchange cellulose
H Reeve Angel & Co Ltd

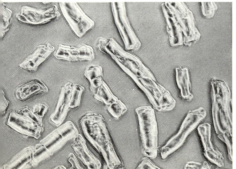

Plate 2 (above) The effect of particle size of the medium can be seen from the separation of cytidine, cytosine and cytidylic acid on columns of different grades of Sephadex G-25. On the coarse grade only cytidine and cytidylic acid were chromatographed. In practice the coarser grades are used for easily resolved mixtures and industrial purposes.

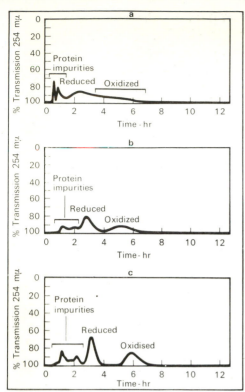

a Old fibrous cellulose   b Whatman advanced fibrous
ion-exchange cellulose CM 23   c Whatman
microgranular ion-exchange cellulose CM 52
H Reeve Angel & Co Ltd

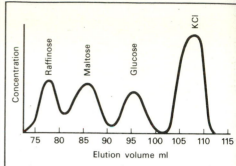

Desalting and separation of raffinose, maltose and glucose
on a column of Sephadex G-15 using 0·025 M phosphate
buffer, pH 7
Pharmacia Fine Chemicals

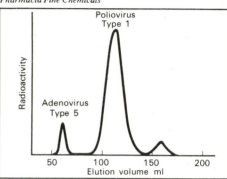

Separation of radioactively labelled viruses on a column of
Sepharose 2B using phosphate buffer, pH 7·2
Pharmacia Fine Chemicals

Plate 3 (above left) The effect of microstructure is apparent from the different separations of
Cytochrome C (an iron-containing protein found in heart muscle) on columns containing various
types of carboxymethyl cellulose. The oxidised and reduced forms of Cytochrome C have the same
molecular weight and differ only by a single charge.

The higher resolution achieved with the microgranular form is a result of its particular
microstructure. On the other hand, the advanced fibrous form is able to stand higher rates of
solvent flow in columns and is more suitable when higher resolution is secondary to speed.

Plate 4 Gel-filtration (above right) The fractionation of mixtures of molecules with different
molecular weights is a valuable property of gel-filtration techniques. By a suitable choice of medium,
substances of almost any molecular weight right up to virus particles, can be separated.

Plate 5 Gel-filtration in organic solvents The fractionation of water-insoluble substances by
gel-filtration in organic solvents can be conducted with a number of media. Two typical separations
are shown below. The figure on the left shows the separation of glycerol esters (fats) on a column of
Sephadex LH-20 using chloroform as the solvent, while the other figure is of a similar type of
separation on a column of Styragel using benzene.

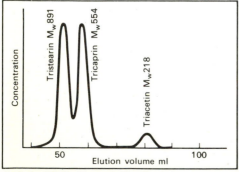

Sephadex LH 20. *Pharmacia Fine Chemicals*

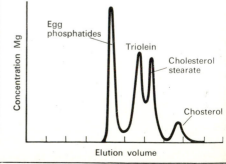

Styragel. *Waters Associates*

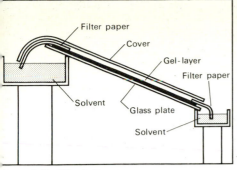

Plate 6 (left) The experimental set-up for thin-layer gel-filtration.

Filter paper
Cover
Gel-layer
Filter paper
Solvent
Glass plate
Solvent

harmacia Fine Chemicals

Plate 7 (below) Gas chromatography: separations on Porasil Porasil (spherical porous silica beads) has many advantages over the commonly used inorganic supports. Chemical inertness and a choice of pore size and surface area allow it to be used with or without liquid coatings. Some typical separations are shown below. By selecting the proper type of Porasil, the effect of the solid support can be adjusted to obtain the best separation.

as chromatography
Waters Associates

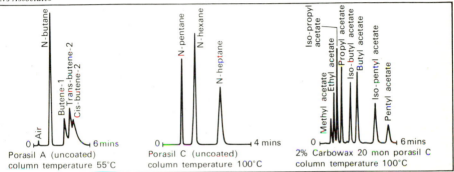

Porasil A (uncoated) column temperature 55°C

Porasil C (uncoated) column temperature 100°C

2% Carbowax 20 mon porasil C column temperature 100°C

Plate 8 Gas chromatography: separations on Porapak (below) Although they are solid, Porapak porous polymer beads for GLC have the partition properties of a highly extended liquid surface. The basic polymer beads can be modified in a number of ways to give types with different separating characteristics. This type of medium is particularly valuable for the separation of the more polar compounds such as water, alcohols, glycols, amines, organic acids, etc., although it can also be used for hydrocarbons and permanent gases. A number of separations on this material is shown below.

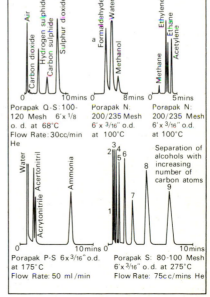

Porapak Q-S: 100-120 Mesh 6' x 1/8 o. d. at 68°C Flow Rate: 30cc/min He

Porapak N. 200/235 Mesh 6' x 3/16" o.d. at 100°C

Porapak N: 200/235 Mesh 6' x 3/16" o.d. at 100°C

Porapak P-S 6 x 3/16" o.d. at 175°C Flow Rate: 50 ml/min

Porapak S: 80-100 Mesh 6' x 3/16" o. d. at 275°C Flow Rate: 75cc/mins He

Separation of alcohols with increasing number of carbon atoms

Gas chromatography. *Waters Associates*

Plate 9 The Aimer universal outfit for paper chromatography This apparatus was specially designed to allow both one and two dimensional separations to be performed. It is based on an all glass tank, 30 cm cube, into which fits a frame which will accommodate 5 larger or up to 50 smaller sheets for development by the ascending method. The lower photograph also shows that it can be readily converted for development by the descending technique. (Designed by Dr. Ivor Smith.)

Paper Chromatography
Aimer Products

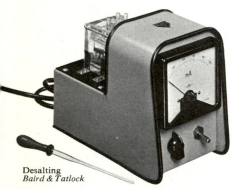

Plate 10 BTL desalting apparatus This small, self-contained unit is extremely valuable for removing salts, particularly from biological solutions, prior to chromatography. The mode of operation is described briefly on page 18.

Desalting
Baird & Tatlock

Location
CAMAG

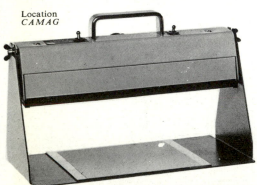

Plate 11 The CAMAG ultraviolet lamp
Ultraviolet light reveals many substances on paper or thin-layer chromatograms which are invisible in ordinary light. The portable CAMAG apparatus provides two lamps radiating short wave (25.4 nm) and longer wave (35.6 nm) UV light, which enables compounds to be located by normal fluorescence or by quenching on TLC plates containing a fluorescent additive. The lamp would normally be used in a darkened area.

Plate 12(a) CAMAG thin-layer electrophoresis cell
The CAMAG thin-layer electrophoresis cell and the high voltage equipment (opposite) allow electrophoresis to be conducted under different conditions and with a wide range of media.

Thin-layer electrophoresis has many of the advantages of thin-layer chromatography and is often used in conjunction with it. Advantages include shorter separating times, more distinct spots and a higher separating capacity.

In the cell, the plate, after dampening with buffer, is placed on the water-cooled block. Current-conducting wicks also dampened with buffer then complete the contact between the glass buffer troughs at either end through the plate. A voltage gradient is then applied by connecting the electrodes in the troughs to a power pack supplying up to 500–1 000 volts. Separations usually take from ½–2 hours.

Electrophoresis. *CAMAG*

Plate 12(b) CAMAG high-voltage electrophoresis (HVE) equipment A tremendous amount of heat is produced when electrophoresis is carried out with high voltages (up to 5 000 volts), so one has to have relatively thin material such as paper and a very efficient cooling system. The CAMAG HVE cell features one of the most efficient cooling systems ever developed and is principally designed for use with paper strips which are pressed onto the cooling plate by means of an inflatable polythene bag. Because of the dangerous voltages, the cell fits into an outer safety case having a large window to facilitate observation.

Electrophoresis. *CAMAG*

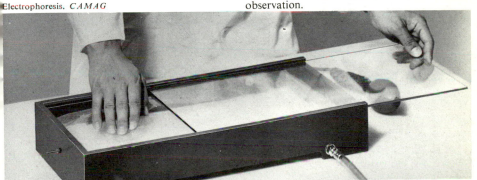

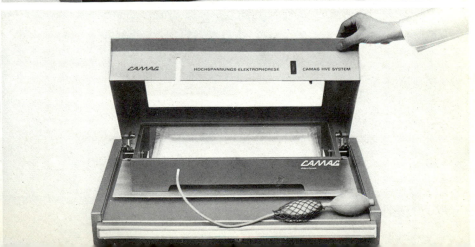

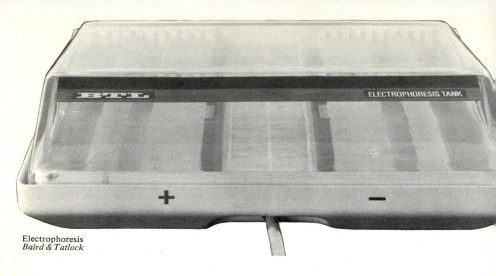

Electrophoresis
Baird & Tatlock

Plate 13 The BTL electrophoresis apparatus
The tank above is specially constructed to accept
paper or cellulose acetate sheets or a single
20×20 cm thin-layer plate. Power is supplied by
the high stability power pack which incorporates
many novel features including transistorised
current and voltage control circuits which allow
constant current or constant voltage to be
selected. The pack automatically adjusts its
output to account for changes in load
characteristics.

Electrophoresis
Baird & Tatlock

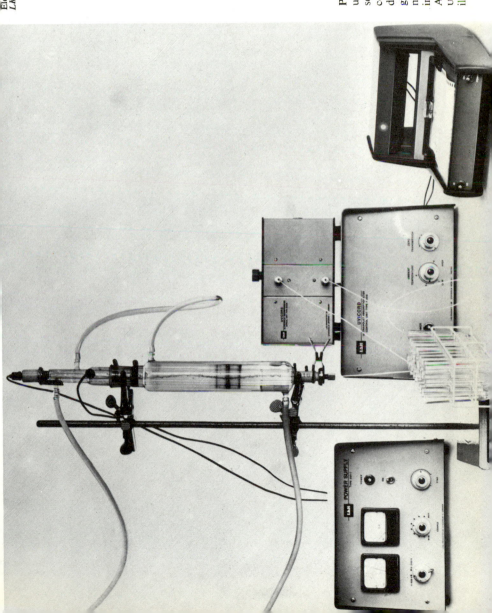

Electrolytic focusing
LKB

Plate 14 Electrolytic focusing This is a unique development of electrolysis for the separation of proteins and other biological compounds. It makes use of the fact that differences in the ratio of acidic/basic groups in the molecules of the substances make them migrate to different positions in the column when a voltage is applied. Also included in the photograph is the UVICORD, an instrument of the type illustrated in Fig. 31, and a recorder (right).

Plate 15 Quickfit thin-layer chromatography apparatus The Quickfit TLC apparatus contains all that is necessary to perform thin-layer chromatographic experiments. One basic necessity of modern TLC techniques is a device to hold plates of varying thicknesses so that their upper surfaces are all in the same plane, ensuring that each plate receives the same thickness of substrate. The automatic plate leveller (shown open right and in use below) achieves this by locating bars which press plates down onto a resilient surface bed on turning the handle. The layer is then applied by means of the spreader which has accurately machined slots of 0.25, 0.50, 0.75 and 1.0 mm.

Plates, once produced, can be dried and then developed in the stainless steel plate racks which fit inside the glass tanks. Each rack is provided with two lifting handles, one to carry the plates horizontally for drying, the other for carrying them vertically for development. The tanks and their lids are ground flat to provide air-tight vessels.

The set also includes a spray and the very useful template and scriber (lower right).

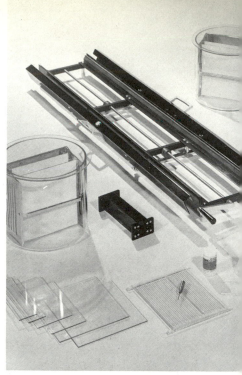

TLC
Quickfit & Quartz

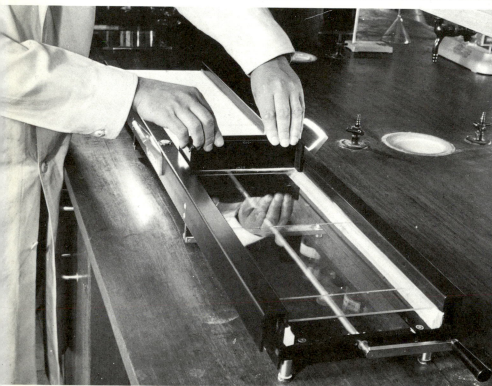

Plate 16 The CAMAG plate coater The plate coater is available as both the hand-operated model shown right, or the automatic model. Both instruments have the floating gate suspended in a floating hopper. This gives reproducible layers immaterial of the thickness or width of the plate. The hand coater can be operated with one finger. The automatic model coats one plate every two seconds.

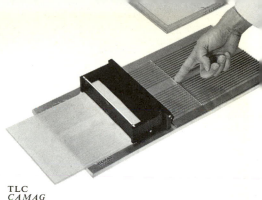

TLC
CAMAG

Plate 17 The BTL motorised coater Although incorporation of a motor may seem an unnecessary elaboration of a simple technique, experience has shown that the thickness of the layer depends not only on the gap setting but also on the speed at which the plate passes under the coating edge. The motor drive gives a more uniform speed and hence more uniform coatings.

TLC
Baird & Tatlock

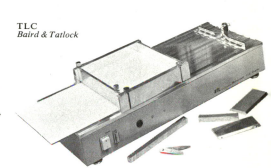

Plate 18 The CAMAG sandwich chamber showing a plate in the course of development. Advantages over tanks include the small quantity of solvent required and the ideally saturated vapour within the chamber.

TLC
CAMAG

Plate 19 The CAMAG chromatocharger (see p. 38) The chromatocharger allows a known volume of liquid to be applied to a plate as a narrow uniform band. This gives cleaner separations than when application is done by hand, and thus makes it ideal for both quantitative and preparative work.

(see p. 38)

TLC
CAMAG

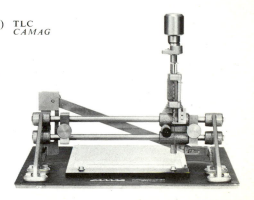

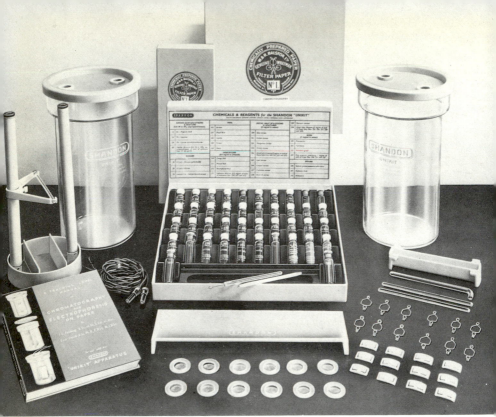

Shandon Unikit No. 1

Plate 20 Shandon UNIKIT No. 1 teaching apparatus (above) Easy-to-use apparatus, specially designed for step-by-step instruction in the principles of chromatography and electrophoresis on paper. 55 graded experiments are detailed in the comprehensive teaching manual, which also includes a section on thin-layer chromatography. The equipment has been found useful for small scale laboratory work.

Shandon UNIKIT No. 2 teaching apparatus (below) An ingenious set of simple equipment for carrying out 14 graded experiments in TLC including a teaching manual, which explains the principles and practice in straightforward, easily understandable terms.

Shandon Unikit No. 2

Shandon Scientific Co Ltd

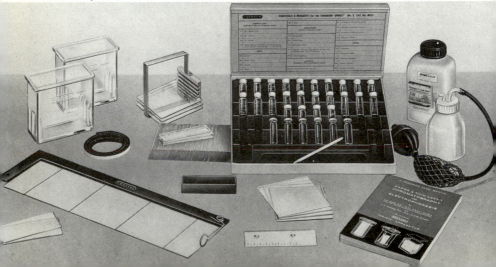

Plate 21 The Kodak mini TLC kit with precoated sheets (right) The Eastman Chromatogram kit, model 104, is specially designed to illustrate the principles of TLC quickly and simply in classrooms or laboratories. The kit contains 25 sheets precoated with silica-gel with a fluorescent indicator, a developing apparatus of the sandwich chamber type, a bottle containing a mixture of dyes in solution and the instruction book.

Plate 22 Polygram precoated TLC sheets (right) MN *Polygram* prepared foils for TLC offer all the advantages of both thin-layer and paper chromatography. The foils are flexible; they can be cut to any desired size with scissors, and may be stored in normal conditions. Foils layered with silica-gel, cellulose powder, ion-exchange powders, aluminium oxide and polyamide are available.

Plate 23 The Quickfit TLC demonstration kit (right) This kit contains all the equipment necessary to produce small TLC plates for class experiments. Illustrated are the aluminium plate support, the mini spreader and a spray.

Plate 24 Applied science TLC kit (below) This kit offers everything necessary to get started in TLC. The low cost of the complete kit and its sturdy nature make it ideal for instructional as well as more serious research purposes. The kit includes an aerosol spray unit and comes complete with an instruction booklet.

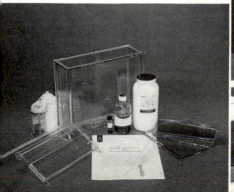

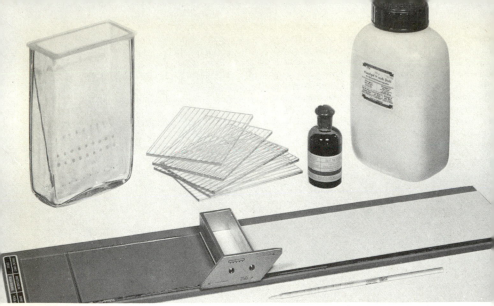

Camlab

Plate 25 The Desaga mini TLC set The mini set is recommended for teaching in schools or where TLC is required at infrequent intervals. The small template accepts three plates together with starting and finishing plates, and coating is carried out in the usual way with the mini-spreader.

Plate 26 The Mallinckrodt chroma teaching kit TM A complete elementary teaching kit housed in polystyrene box for ease of storage. The instruction manual offers simple instruction in TLC and sets out in clear form nine experiments, each subdivided into Objective–Procedure–Discussion.

Camlab

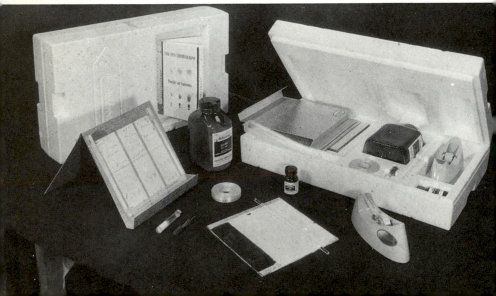

Plate 27 Desaga chromato-tubes An intriguing development in chromatography, the Desaga chromato-tubes consist of glass tubes, the inner surface of which has been coated with an adsorbent. Spots are applied by means of capillary tube and a special holder, and then the tube is fitted into its glass developing base. The volume of the unit is constant and results are reproducible. Tubes, once used, may be eluted overnight, and after reactivation can be used again.

Camlab

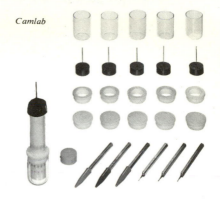

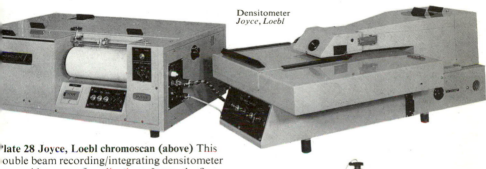

Densitometer
Joyce, Loebl

Plate 28 Joyce, Loebl chromoscan (above) This double beam recording/integrating densitometer has a wide range of applications. It was the first instrument to be used for quantitative measurements of thin-layer chromatograms and both fluorescence and visible techniques. In electrophoresis analysis, the chromoscan evaluates samples run on all media, including paper, starch, agar, cellulose acetate, acrylamide and thin layer strips.

A number of attachments make the chromoscan an extremely versatile instrument. Its design gives a degree of accuracy which makes it useful for repetitive clinical tests. It is in fact particularly suitable for biochemical work, and has figured prominently in work on ribonucleic acids.

The unit on the right of the photograph is the scanner and the result of a scan can be seen on the chart paper.

Plate 29 Chromatographic column Pharmacia produce a wide range of precision columns for use with their gel-filtration media. The K 100/100 illustrated on the right is one of the largest and is intended for preparative work. The column has an integral water jacket and allows bed volumes of between 4 to 7 dm^3.

Columns
Pharmacia

Ion exchange. *BDH*

Plate 30 BDH ready-to-use ion exchange columns
The kit contains six different Amberlite resins contained in plastic tubes fitted with end adaptors. With a piece of tubing and a couple of screw clips one can make an ion exchange column in a matter of seconds. The kit comes complete with a booklet and is ideal for teaching purposes.

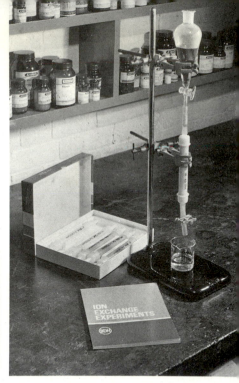

Column chromatography *LKB*

Plate 31 Two modern fraction collectors These two designs differ quite markedly from the simple apparatus shown on p. 46. The BTL Chroafrac (below) has a new and unique system which enables fractions down to 0·1 ml to be collected. The Chromapump (below left), Chromafrac (below centre) and timer together provide a means of cutting fractions from the inlet side, since eluent delivery and fraction collecting are directly linked. The LKB UltroRac (opposite) is the smallest fraction collector with 200 standard test-tube capacity. The UltroRac has a number of sophisticated features and its rugged design is guaranteed for three years.

Column chromatography *BTL*

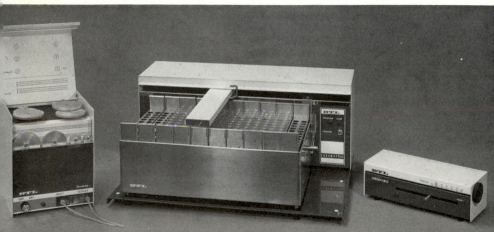

Gas chromatography
mer Products

Gas chromatography
Perkin-Elmer

Plate 32 The Perkin-Elmer model F11 gas chromatograph with high performance oven **(right)** This chromatograph is constructed on the modular principle so that other units (such as other detection system or for programming) can be added as required. In use the instrument would also be connected to a recorder. The very precise oven control is necessary if quantitative accuracy is to be achieved. The coiled column can just be seen inside the partially open oven.

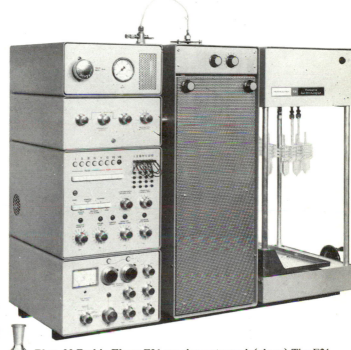

Plate 33 Perkin-Elmer F21 gas chromatograph (above) The F21 preparative chromatograph is a bench-top instrument designed for either manual or automatic operation, and can be used as a preparative or analytical instrument. When used preparatively, only a small portion of the sample (less than 5 %) is passed through the flame ionisation detector.

Plate 34 The Aimer educational gas chromatograph (left) A complete system which provides the teacher with all that is required for a suitable introduction to this subject. It is simply and inexpensively constructed from a glass column with a heating jacket to enable separations to be carried out at various temperatures. There are three detection systems, two visual (titration and flame) and one electrical (katharometer). To provide the teacher with a complete teaching unit a short textbook and a single concept film have been prepared. (Designed by D. R. Browning.)

Perkin-Elmer

Plate 35 Gas chromatograph-mass spectrometer combinations The Perkin-Elmer (above) and
LKB (below) instruments are two examples of these very powerful tools. By combining the
separating ability of GLC with the structural determining capacity of mass spectrometry,
fantastically difficult analyses can sometimes be performed in just a few hours.

LKB

distance dropped by the plunger —and hence the amount of liquid dispensed by the syringe — may be varied to suit particular requirements. Because the syringe needle never touches the plate there is no possibility of damaging the layer. In an alternative device designed by Professor Stahl, the sample is transferred to the plate with the aid of an inert gas or compressed air.

These applicators are excellent, but are rather expensive for student demonstrations. Another simple method of getting narrow bands is to apply the sample in a band by a suitable procedure and then to develop the plate a short way in a polar solvent prior to the actual separation.

4.6 Development of thin layers

Development of solid layers is usually carried out by the ascending method in suitable tanks like the one shown in Fig. 24. If more than one or two plates are being developed at the same time, they can be stacked in a rack and developed in a slightly larger tank as shown in Plate 15.

Whichever method is selected, a sheet of solvent–impregnated paper is placed round the sides of the tank to ensure that the atmosphere inside is saturated with vapour. The bottom of the tank is covered with the solvent to a depth of 0.5–1 cm and, after a suitable period to allow equilibrium to be reached, the plate is introduced. The lid is kept firmly in place while the plate is developed.

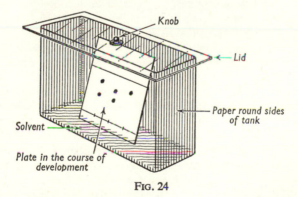

FIG. 24

When using single solvents for development, the size and shape of the tank has little effect, but with mixed solvents and large tanks there is a danger that the solvent, in equilibrium with a relatively large volume of vapour phase, will be different from that originally intended. One way of getting round this difficulty is to use special little tanks known as *sandwich chambers*. The CAMAG sandwich chamber and a plate in the course of development are shown in Plate 18.

In a sandwich chamber the coated plate is used as one of the walls, and a similar sized plate and a cardboard spacer, or a cover plate with fused glass sides, complete the chamber. The sides are clamped securely together with clips. Once assembled, the chamber is placed in a trough to allow development. One feature of this method is that only very small quantities of solvent are required.

The sandwich chamber principle is the one favoured for the development of chromatosheets.

Usually the solvent front is allowed to ascend about 10 cm above the origin before the plate or sheet is removed. The solvent front is carefully marked with a sharp pencil. The solvent in the layer evaporates within a few minutes. Heat can be applied if necessary, and then the plate is ready for location of the compounds.

With very delicate layers such as gel filtration beads, the layers should be run by descending chromatography in a closed chamber, using an experimental set–up like the one shown in Plate 6. An angle of 10°–20° has been found to be the most suitable.

If a commercially-produced tank is not available, development can be performed quite adequately in ordinary powder bottles or the screw-capped jars sold for jam making.

4.7 Location of compounds on chromatograms

Location procedures are similar to those used on paper chromatograms, with certain notable differences. To begin with, location by the dipping method is not recommended as layers can easily be disturbed by this procedure. An advantage of most thin layers is that, being of a purely inorganic nature, very corrosive reagents such as concentrated sulphuric acid and powerful oxidising agents can be used for the location of compounds on them.

Another very useful reagent is iodine vapour. The developed chromatogram is placed in a tank with a few crystals of iodine on the bottom, and left for a few minutes. The iodine tends to accumulate at points where the compounds are, so that one gets dark brown spots on a pale yellowish backround. As long as the substances on the plate will not react with iodine, this is an excellent, non-destructive location procedure.

Other non-destructive methods for locating compounds include fluorescence and radioactivity. As many thin layer plates have fluorescent additives to reveal compounds by their quenching of fluorescence in addition to natural fluorescence, the former is particularly useful. A lamp for viewing chromatograms under long and short wavelength ultraviolet light is shown in Plate 11.

4.8 Preparative and quantitative thin layer chromatography

By using somewhat thicker layers and wider plates, thin layer chromatography can be used as an excellent preparative tool. The amount of material which can be chromatographed on a single plate obviously depends upon the nature of the material and the mode of separation. As a general rule 100 mg of the average mixture can be fractionated on a plate 40 × 20 cm (1 mm layer) by adsorption, but only 10 mg by partition. By developing several plates together, however, quite large amounts of material can be purified.

The sample is usually applied as a long streak along the baseline, using one of the streakers previously described. The plates are then developed in a suitable solvent. It should be remembered that the thicker layers can remove quite a lot of solvent, so that there are dangers of changes in solvent composition during development.

Location of the separated components is best done by one of the non-destructive methods or with the aid of iodine vapour. If this is not desirable or possible, side strips on the plate can be located with a suitable chemical reagent. The bands of required substances can then be removed.

The simplest method of removing the layer is to scrape off an appropriate area with the tip of a spatula, and then extract the substance from the powder with a solvent. Alternatively, a device like a little vacuum cleaner can be purchased, which sucks the powder into a thimble. The substance can then be recovered by Soxhlet extraction. In the case of chromatosheets, the desired zone can be cut out with a pair of scissors and the substance recovered in much the same way as with paper strips.

Quantitative thin layer chromatography can be performed in two basically different ways. One way is to apply a known volume of the sample to a plate and develop, locate and recover the separated material as described above. The isolated material can then be determined by any of the usual methods of analysis. Another way is to determine the separated components *on* the plate. The principles involved have already been discussed in Section 3.13, to which readers are referred.

4.9 Documentation of thin layer chromatograms

The storage of thin layer chromatograms is difficult and usually undesirable, since the plates are used time and time again. One has therefore to find some means of recording the results obtained. The pattern of spots or bands after location can be photographed or traced but, although the former is excellent, both are tedious and time-consuming in normal circumstances. A more convenient method is to spray the layer with a specially prepared plastic dispersion which hardens to give a clear plastic coating. The thin, flexible film which results can be removed from the glass plate and stored almost indefinitely.

The chromatosheets, on the other hand, are fairly resistant to abrasion, and can be stored without treatment if a certain amount of care is exercised in handling them.

5 Column Chromatography

Numerous media are used inside columns, separations being effected by partition, adsorption and ion-exchange. Almost any medium can be used, and common ones include cellulose, silica gel, Celite and kieselguhr (for separations by partition), alumina, magnesium oxide, calcium oxide, charcoal, various ion exchange resins and cellulose derivatives (for separations by adsorption and ion exchange).

In all cases, optimum results can only be attained if care is taken in a selection of the medium. The physical state of this should be such that it allows uniform packing of the column and a free flow of solvent through it.

5.1 Packing the column

For larger scale laboratory separations a column of the type shown in Fig. 25(a) is used, the size of the column being determined by the quantity of mixture being fractionated.

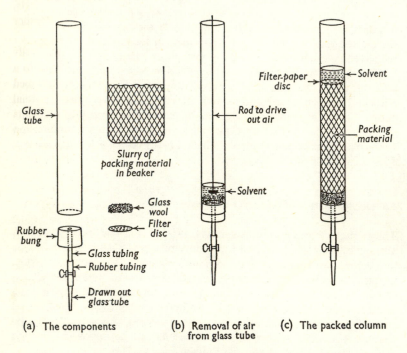

(a) The components

(b) Removal of air
from glass tube

(c) The packed column

Fig. 25. Making up a column

Chromatographic columns can be purchased in a number of sizes and with a variety of refinements, or they can equally effectively be assembled from simple materials found in the laboratory. The end of the tube can be closed with a rubber bung, or, better still, drawn out so that it will accommodate a short length of rubber tubing which can be controlled with a screw-clip.

The first step in setting up a column is to clamp it in a vertical position. Next a porcelain disc (if available) is placed in the bottom of the column followed by a small quantity of glass wool. These retain solid materials in the column while allowing liquids to percolate freely through them.

The medium to be used in the column can be poured in dry, but wet packing is far more common. In wet packing the medium is introduced as a thick slurry in a suitable liquid medium. A little of the pure liquid is first poured into the tube to a depth of a few inches. Air gets trapped in the glass wool and has to be removed by pushing it with a long glass rod. The slurry is poured into the tube a little at a time and allowed to separate under gravity until a column of the correct height is obtained. Finally the tap at the bottom of the column is opened to allow the liquid to run out until it just covers the top of the medium. The column is then ready for the introduction of the sample and the start of the separation.

5.2 Solvents used with columns

Three groups of solvent are used with columns for separations by partition, adsorption or ion-exchange.

Solvents used for partition are similar to those described in previous sections.

For separations on adsorption materials, the purity of the solvent is very important since impurities can alter the complete course of development. With adsorbents such as alumina and silica gel the strength of adsorption increases with increasing polar nature of the material added; the latter is therefore normally added in a non-polar solvent, e.g. petrol because polar groups such as hydroxyl-OH in water and ethanol would cause desorption. Elution of the column can therefore be carried out using solvents of increasingly polar nature. A typical series is as follows: pure water > methanol > ethanol > acetone > ethyl acetate > diethyl ether > chloroform > benzene > cyclohexane > hexane. The opposite effect occurs with charcoal as adsorbent, so that the above series will, in general, be reversed. With activated charcoal, adsorption frequently takes place from aqueous solution. Thus, if an aqueous solution containing the sugars glucose and maltose (a disaccharide consisting of two glucose units) is poured on to a charcoal column, the sugar molecules are adsorbed on the charcoal and can be eluted using water (for glucose) and weak aqueous ethanol (for maltose).

Separations on ion-exchange materials are usually effected by pouring the sample in aqueous solution on to the top of an ion-exchange column where the components become adsorbed by electrostatic forces. They are then selectively desorbed by altering the pH or the concentration of salt (ions) in the eluting solvent.

5.3 Separation techniques

PARTITION COLUMNS: The mixture to be separated is dissolved in a suitable solvent to give a fairly concentrated solution which is introduced into the column by means of a pipette. The solvent chosen must be miscible with the solvent used to pack the column. Introduction is aided if a glass rod is held as shown in Fig. 26(*a*).

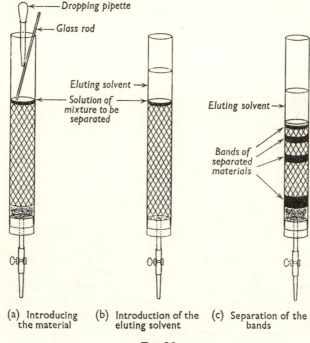

(a) Introducing the material   (b) Introduction of the eluting solvent   (c) Separation of the bands

FIG. 26

The clip at the bottom is opened slightly to allow sufficient liquid to run out until the level of the sample just reaches the top of the packing material. The eluting solvent (eluant) is then added and allowed to flow steadily through the medium, adjusting the clip to give the required rate. The flow is continued until the mixture is completely separated into its components.

This type of procedure is called *elution analysis* and is the only one used with partition columns. It is illustrated in Fig. 26.

ADSORPTION COLUMNS: Separations may be achieved with adsorption columns in exactly the same way as described above, but variations in the eluting procedure are very valuable in some cases. If, for example, the first solvent only readily elutes a proportion of the components in the mixture, leaving some adsorbed on the column, a second solvent with stronger desorbing power will be required to complete the separation. Sometimes a series of solvents (each one having a stronger desorbing power than the previous one) are necessary. Because the solvents are introduced in a stepwise fashion a procedure of this kind is referred to as *stepwise elution*.

As an alternative to stepwise elution, the concentration of the second solvent can be increased uniformly using an apparatus like the one in

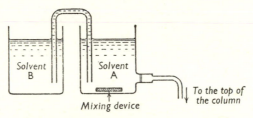

FIG. 27 The apparatus for gradient elution

Fig. 27. The liquid flowing through the column has a slowly increasing desorbing power and therefore it successively desorbs the compounds from the column. This procedure, called *gradient elution* is particularly useful for separations on ion-exchange materials.

5.4 Examination and identification of compounds

When the sample applied to the column has coloured components, it is a fairly easy matter to visualise the progress of a separation, but with colourless substances it is more difficult. Two approaches can be made to the identification and isolation of compounds separated on columns. The simplest method is to carry out elution for a suitable period and then push the packing material out of the column. After allowing the eluting solvent to evaporate off, the column can be cut up into slices, each slice extracted, and the extract examined. Alternatively a strip of paper can be pressed against the extruded column so that it absorbs a little of the solvent. When dry, the

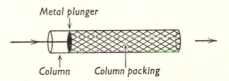

FIG. 28. Extrusion of the column

paper is sprayed with a reagent to locate the compounds, and therefore, by fitting the paper back on to the column, the position of each compound can be found and the corresponding sections cut from the column. Procedures of this kind are not widely used but they have the advantage of being far more economical with the (often very expensive) eluting solvent.

The second and most widely used technique is to allow the separation to continue further so that the separated compounds emerge in the *eluate*. In practice, a large number of small fractions of eluate (usually of equal volume) is collected and analysed by a suitable method. When their contents are known, some of the fractions can be combined and concentrated, while others can be rejected because they contain no useful

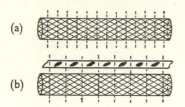

(a)

(b)

FIG. 29a. Slicing the column
FIG. 29b. Matching the paper

material. Some fractions may contain several components and require refractionation on another column. The purity of compounds obtained in this manner can be checked by chromatography on paper or thin layers using several different solvents.

The collection of a large number of liquid fractions is both arduous and time consuming so that, in practice, some form of mechanical device is employed. A fraction collector is shown in Fig. 30. It consists of a turntable in which a series of collection tubes are placed. The turntable is turned by an electrical device which, in its simplest form, moves the tubes along at regular time intervals. It is more convenient, however, to collect fractions containing a known volume or a set number of drops.

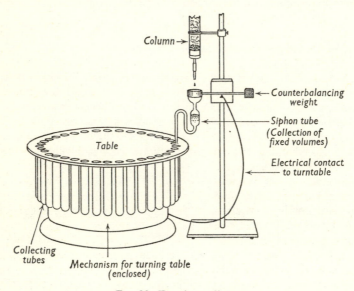

Column →

Counterbalancing weight

Siphon tube (Collection of fixed volumes)

Electrical contact to turntable

Table

Collecting tubes

Mechanism for turning table (enclosed)

FIG. 30. Fraction collector

Fig. 30 shows a siphon tube which is used to collect fixed volumes of eluant. In this apparatus the tube is counterbalanced by a weight to form a kind of 'see-saw'. This weight is such that, when the siphon tube is approximately half-full, it tips the balance and in so doing activates an electrical device which moves a fresh collecting tube into position. When the correct volume has been collected, the liquid siphons from the tube causing the weight to drop again. This process is repeated until sufficient fractions have been collected.

In an alternative device known as a *drop-counter*, drops of the eluant pass through a beam of light which activates a photoelectric cell. The device can be adjusted so that a preset number of drops pass before a fresh tube is moved under the column outlet. Drop-counters are particularly useful when very small fractions are being collected, but they are equally efficient with larger fractions. As the solvent passing through the column changes, or as compounds emerge in the eluant, the drop size changes, so that these do not always allow constant volumes to be collected.

Having collected a number of fractions, there still remains the problem of analysing the contents of each of the tubes. With hundreds of tubes, which is not uncommon with some separations, this is a formidable task.

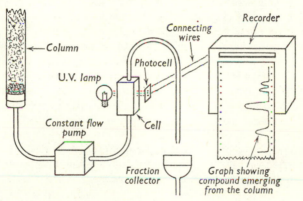

FIG. 31. Continuous monitoring of eluant

In cases like these the eluant is often 'monitored' continuously, before it enters the fraction collector.

For continuous monitoring, the eluant is led directly into a device which measures some property of the compounds which are being separated. Many compounds, for example, although colourless, absorb light in the ultraviolet region. In this case the eluant is pumped at a constant rate through a cell with windows on two sides. A beam of ultraviolet light of a particular wavelength passes through the solution and falls on a photo-electric cell at the other side. In some machines the amount of light falling on the photocell is measured automatically at regular intervals and the results punched out on a sheet of moving graph paper. The presence of compounds which absorb ultraviolet light in the eluant will cause peaks to occur on the graph so that by consulting the graph, fractions containing useful material can readily be located.

Alternatively, if the compunds being separated do not have the property of absorbing ultraviolet light, and many of course do not, they can usually be reacted with an appropriate reagent to produce coloured products, which can again be monitored by a suitable photoelectric device. For preparative purposes, only a proportion of the eluant would be treated in this manner, while the remainder would be collected in fractions. The fractions containing useful material can then be readily determined by consulting the chromatogram.

If the monitoring and the chromatographic separation are carried out under carefully controlled conditions, the chromatogram can be used to obtain quantitative results. In perhaps the most famous of the quantitative column chromatographic techniques — the automatic amino acid analyser — amino acids present in protein hydrolysates, physiological fluids and tissue extracts are separated on an ion-ecxhange column by means of buffer changes. The eluant leaving the column containing the separated amino acids is continuoulsy mixed with a ninhydrin solution, and the mixture pumped through a long coiled tube contained in a heated bath to develop the coloured reaction products.

Normal α–amino acids produce a violet colour, while inimo acids, which are also often present, produce a yellow coloration. The absorbtion of the solution is therefore read at two different wavelengths, 440 nm for the imino acids, and 570 nm for the α-amino acids. Often the absorption at 570 nm is measured with long and short cuvette lengths, to ensure the accuracy of readings at both high and low amino acid concentrations. In commercial machines, three separate absorbance curves are plotted, usually in different coloured dots.

The amount of any particular amino acid present in a given sample can be determined by comparing the area under the appropriate curve on the chromatogram with that produced by a known amount of the same amino acid on another chromatogram run previously.

5.5. Moving wire liquid chromatography

The moving wire liquid chromatograph is a relatively recent development. In this apparatus, a high-precision stainless steel wire passes through the column effluent, picking up a thin coating of liquid. The wire passes into an evaporator oven where the solvent is driven off, and then into a pyrolyser oven which sweeps any vaporisable or pyrolysable compounds into a very sensitive detector of the type originally developed for gas chromatography. This may be either an argon ionisation detector or a flame ionisation detector, depending upon the type of sample being analysed.

The high sensitivity of these detectors to organic compounds, coupled with their insensitivity to small temperature and gas flowrate changes, enables minute quantities, as little as fractions of a part per million relative to the solvent, to be detected and recorded.

The response of this kind of system is very rapid, so that the peaks are recorded on the chromatogram almost as soon as the compounds leave the column, thus allowing a careful watch to be kept on the separation. Because only a minute fraction of the sample is required for monitoring, virtually all of the separated components can be recovered.

The moving wire system can be employed with all types of column, but it is limited to separations of vaporisable or pyrolysable organic compounds. The solvent must also have a much lower boiling point than the solutes, and generally it must have a lower surface tension than water to ensure even coating of the wire. If these conditions are met, the system has the big advantage of being independent of solvent so that even changes in the eluting solvents, as for example in gradient or stepwise elution, have no effect on results.

This kind of system enables certain inherent advantages of column chromatography over thin layer and gas chromatography to be exploited. For example, it allows analyses to be made, at or near room temperature, of substances which would be decomposed at the high temperatures required by gas-liquid chromatography (GLC). In other cases it could allow samples to be analysed directly, whereas for GLC it would be necessary to produce more volatile derivatives.

The high sensitivity of the detection system also allows high stationary phase/sample ratios, approaching those of thin layer separations, to be achieved. The resolution is consequently superior to that normally found in column chromatography.

5.6 Recycling column chromatography

It is not always possible to obtain a complete separation with a single column, and so it is often desirable to refractionate partially separated material on a second column, using probably a different packing medium and a different solvent system. For very stable compounds this is quite satisfactory, but for the isolation of easily decomposed substances such as enzymes, the process of concentrating and preparing fractions from the first column for application to the second, can be time-consuming and lead to considerable losses. Such losses can sometimes be avoided by using a technique known as *recycling chromatography* (RCC).

The apparatus used for RCC has three principal features:

(*a*) The sample is passed throught the column bed many times thus increasing the effective length, and hence the efficiency of the system.

(*b*) The progress of the separation is continuously observed by means of a non-destructive UV-absorption or conductivity monitoring device.

(*c*) Special selector valves allow completely separated components or unwanted material to be removed from the system at any part of the cycle. Incompletely resolved components can then be recycled until a satisfactory separation has been achieved.

The RCC system can, in theory, be employed for a wide variety of column chromatographic separations, but at present it is used mainly in conjunction with molecular-sieving materials such as Sephadex.

6 Gas Chromatography

The three techniques we have considered so far were devised, and are most suitable for, the separation of solids and non-volatile liquids in solution. *Gas chromatography*, as its name suggests, is particularly suited for the separation of gases and volatile liquids or solids in the gaseous state.

A small sample of the material being examined is injected into a stream of an inert gas such as nitrogen, hydrogen, carbon dioxide, argon or helium which carries it into a column containing a suitable medium capable of

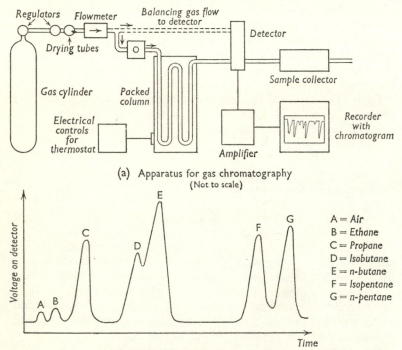

(a) Apparatus for gas chromatography
(Not to scale)

A = Air
B = Ethane
C = Propane
D = Isobutane
E = n-butane
F = Isopentane
G = n-pentane

(b) Chromatogram showing the separation of gases from petroleum oil on alumina using hydrogen as the carrier gas

Fig. 32

retarding the flow, by varying degrees, of the individual components of the sample as they flow through the column. The separated components then emerge from the column at discrete intervals (characteristic of each component) and pass through some form of detector. Differences in adsorption or partition on the material in the column is again the factor which makes separations possible. As a general rule, gas analyses are carried out on adsorption columns (gas/solid chromatography), while liquids and volatile solids are separated on partition columns (gas/liquid chromotography).

Typical examples of the use of gas chromatography are the analysis of petrols and petroleum gases, the analysis of food oils and flavourings and for following organic reactions. It can be used for micro-preparations or, with modified apparatus, large scale preparations also.

Gas chromatography, although basically simple in concept, requires a little more in the way of apparatus and control for general application. An inexpensive apparatus which is capable of demonstrating most of the features of gas chromatography is available commercially and experiments using a simpler form of apparatus are given on page 62.

6.1 The carrier gas

Gases are available in a substantially pure form from steel cylinders where they are kept under pressure. For optimum results it is advisable to dry a gas before use by passing it through tubes containing a material known as a molecular sieve, which selectively removes water vapour from the gas. Carbon dioxide is usually prepared from 'dry ice'.

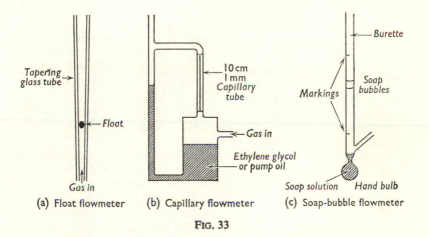

(a) Float flowmeter (b) Capillary flowmeter (c) Soap-bubble flowmeter

FIG. 33

The choice of carrier gas depends upon the nature of the sample and the type of detector being employed. Hydrogen and helium, for example, are particularly suited for use with a thermal conductivity type of detector (katharometer) because they both possess high thermal conductivity, and hence allow a rapid response by the detector.

The rate of flow of the carrier gas through the apparatus is controlled by means of a special valve and is measured by a device known as a *flowmeter*, three of which are shown in Fig. 33.

(a) Float flowmeter

When no gas is flowing through the meter, the small float remains at the bottom of a tapering vertical glass tube. In use, the float is forced up the tube until its own weight balances the upthrust of gas flowing through the meter. The vertical height of the float, therefore, continuously (and fairly accurately) denotes the rate of flow.

(b) Capillary flowmeter

The capillary flowmeter measures the pressure developed in forcing the gas to pass through a length of capillary tubing. This is directly proportional to the flow rate.

(c) Soap-bubble flowmeter

Soap bubbles are generated by gently pressing the bulb at the bottom until the soap solution momentarily covers the inlet. The time taken by a bubble to move along a given length of tube provides a measurement of flow rate.

The soap-bubble flowmeter is placed at the outlet of the column and not as shown in Fig. 32(a).

6.2 Introduction of the sample

The actual amount introduced will depend upon the nature and concentration of the solutes, the size of the column and the type and sensitivity of the detector system, but generally only small samples are used for analytical gas chromatography. The usual range is from 0.1–10 mm³ for gases and liquids to fractions of milligrams for solids. Larger samples tend to lead to poor separations.

Gas and liquid samples are introduced into the carrier gas from a microsyringe or similar device via a self sealing rubber serum cap. A simple example is shown in Figs. 47 and 48.

Solids and viscous liquids are introduced by weighing a small amount in a thin-walled glass ampoule, placing this into the carrier gas stream and then crushing it. Alternatively they can be dissolved in a suitable solvent and introduced in the same way as liquid samples.

One difficulty with relatively non-volatile substances is that there is a danger of the sample's condensing out either at the injection point or at the outlet. To stop this from happening and to ensure that the sample is rapidly vapourised on entry, it is the usual practice to heat the inlet and outlet points by means of an electric coil. A temperature 50°C above the boiling point of the highest boiling component usually suffices. With gases and low-boiling liquids this is not essential.

Many samples are not analysed directly, but are first converted into more volatile derivatives. Fatty acids, for example, are usually analysed as their methyl esters.

6.3 The column

Gas chromatographic separations are usually carried out at elevated temperatures, so that some form of heating and thermostatic control of the columns is required. This is made much easier if the columns are coiled or bent before use.

Columns are made up from a variety of materials including glass, plastics and metals such as copper, cupronickel and stainless steel. Glass tubes are cheap and inert but are fragile and are difficult to coil. Plastic tubes made of polythene or nylon are easily coiled and uncoiled but tend to dissolve organic liquids from the supporting medium inside the column at elevated temperatures. Metal columns, because they are inert and robust and possess good thermal properties, are generally preferred, but are expensive.

For most analyses, columns 1.5–5 m in length and 2–10 mm diameter are chosen.

In a variation known as *capillary gas chromatography*, tubes 10–1 000 feet long and 0.1–1.0 mm diameter are used.

6.4 The column packing

(a) Adsorption columns

Useful adsorption agents for gas analyses include alumina, activated carbon, silica gel and molecular sieves (such as Linde sieve 5A). Columns containing these materials work efficiently at room temperature, and most gas mixtures can be separated on one or other of them.

The use of adsorption columns can be extended to the separation of compounds with higher molecular weights by raising the temperature of the column, and by partially *poisoning* the adsorbent. Poisons are involatile liquids which are applied to the medium and whose purpose is to block some of the 'active' adsorbing sites. If this is not done, some of the substances being separated become too firmly adsorbed on the medium and, instead of passing along the column as separate symmetrical discrete zones, a proportion is retained and *tailing* of the zones and hence incomplete separation results.

(b) Partition columns

The packing material consists of a finely-divided solid supporting medium such as Celite, ground firebrick or glass beads carrying an involatile liquid medium. Silicone oils and greases, apieson grease, dinonylphthalate and polyethylene glycols are popular for this purpose. These partitioning agents should not be confused with the poisons used on adsorption columns. The partitioning agent for a particular separation is chosen to be as chemically similar to the components of the sample as possible.

To prepare the partitioning medium, the required amount of the stationary phase is dissolved in a suitable volatile solvent such as ether, and a known weight of the supporting medium added, stirring thoroughly to get even distribution of the solution. The solvent is then allowed to evaporate off and the medium completely dried.

6.5 Packing the column

Having decided which medium to use, the next stage is packing the column. It is important that the packing should be uniform. To ensure this the material is usually graded by passing through suitable sieves to remove fine and coarse particles. The partitioning agent or poison is then applied and any solvent used in this application, or any residual moisture, removed by heating.

The material is introduced into the column a little at a time, tapping the column continuously until it is filled. The two ends are closed by a small cotton or glass wool plug. Coiling of the column, if required, is carried out at this stage. Coiled metal or glass columns are best filled with the aid of compressed air.

6.6 Detectors

Compounds can be detected in numerous ways. Hydrogen, when used as the carrier gas, can be ignited at the end of the column. Some compounds can be recognised by the colour they impart to the flame on emergence from the column. This method and an extension of it are used in the experimental section of this book (q.v.). By measuring the flame intensity at regular intervals with a photoelectric device (i.e. a photographic exposure meter) a graph can be plotted from which a quantitative estimation of the individual components of a mixture can be made.

Detectors are extremely important in gas chromatographic separations, and a great deal of effort has been expended in their conception and manufacture. One of the simplest is the *Janak nitrometer*, named after the inventor. Pure carbon dioxide is used as the carrier gas, and after emerging from the column it is passed into a strong solution of potassium hydroxide in which it rapidly dissolves. Gaseous substances in the carrier stream which do not dissolve in the potassium hydroxide are collected in a calibrated gas burette and the volume (and hence the amount) of each component measured at atmospheric pressure.

The nitrometer is an example of an *integral* type of detector, and the graph of volume measured against the time after sample injection shown in Fig. 34(*a*) is typical of such detectors.

Most of the common detectors are, by contrast, of the *differential* type. That is, they are arranged so that they give no response when pure carrier gas is flowing through them but, as any component from the column passes through, they give a response which is directly proportional to either the quantity or concentration of that component. When the component has passed, the detector again gives zero response, until a further component emerges. A differential type record is shown in Fig. 34(*b*).

One of the most important differential detectors is the *katharometer* or thermal conductivity detector. In this instrument two identical cells made of brass are used, each one containing a fine platinum or tungsten wire. The effluent from the column flows through one cell and a carefully balanced reference stream of pure carrier gas through the other (Fig. 34(c)). Each of the wires is heated by an electric current from an accumulator. The temperature attained by the wires, and hence their resistance, depends upon the properties of the gas flowing over them, so that a change of

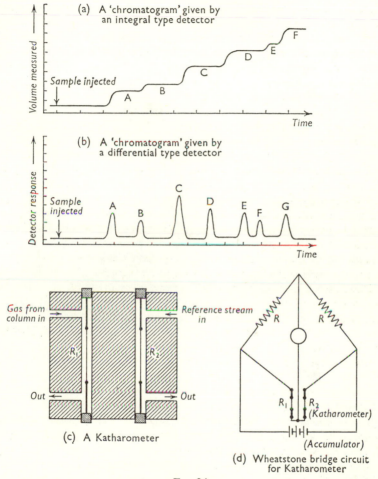

(a) A 'chromatogram' given by an integral type detector

Volume measured

Sample injected

A B C D E F

Time

(b) A 'chromatogram' given by a differential type detector

Detector response

Sample injected

A B C D E F G

Time

Gas from column in

Reference stream in

R_1 R_2

Out Out

(c) A Katharometer

R R

R_1 R_2
(Katharometer)

(Accumulator)

(d) Wheatstone bridge circuit for Katharometer

Fig. 34

composition in the gas flowing through the analytical cell will cause a heat loss and therefore a change in resistance. The wires are arranged to form part of a balanced Wheatstone bridge circuit (Fig. 34(d)), so a component leaving the column unbalances the bridge and gives rise to a deflection on the galvanometer. In most instruments the signal is amplified and causes a pen to move up and down a strip of moving graph paper, thus automatically making a record of the separation. A modern trend is to use thermistors instead of metal wires as they possess certain advantages.

Other differential detectors

Gas density balance

The gas density balance is constructed from a metal block which is bored with a series of tubes in an ingenious manner to form a mechanical analogy of a Wheatstone bridge. This instrument incorporates two channels, the effluent from the column flowing through one and a reference stream through the other.

Compounds from the column passing through the detector set up a small pressure difference across a tube which connects these two channels, and the small gas flow which results is measured with a very sensitive anemometer. The response of the anemometer is a linear function of the concentration and the molecular weight of each component, so the gas density balance can be used to measure either of these two properties (if the other is already known).

Flame temperature detector

In this sensitive and simple detector, nitrogen is used as the carrier gas and a carefully controlled amount of hydrogen is added at the outlet. The mixture is burned to give a fine flame which impinges on a thermocouple set in a quartz tube. The heat of combustion of organic compounds passing through the detector causes an increase in the temperature of the flame, and hence in the e.m.f. generated by the thermocouple. The increase in e.m.f. is detected by a potentiometric method and thus gives a measurement of the amount of any compound passing through the detector. The flame temperature detector is particularly suitable for high molecular weight organic compounds.

Ionisation detectors

The differential detectors described above require careful control of the flowrate of carrier gas, and often of a reference stream as well, because small deviations can produce signals of the same order as those produced by a small amount of eluted vapour. For very sensitive measurements a group of instruments known as *ionisation detectors* are preferred. These have the advantage of not requiring a reference stream.

Components emerging from the column are ionised on entering the detector in some manner (i.e. by a radioactive source or by burning them at high temperature), and this allows the gas in the detector to conduct an electric current, the conductivity being a linear function of the number of ions formed and hence the concentration of eluted vapour in the carrier gas. Pure carrier gas gives virtually no ions and hence no response by the detector.

The most popular detectors of this type are the *argon* and *flame ionisation* detectors.

The flame ionisation detector

In many ways the flame ionisation detector resembles the flame temperature detector mentioned previously. Again nitrogen is used as the carrier gas, hydrogen is added at the outlet and the mixture is burned to give a very fine flame. Instead of measuring the temperature of the flame, however, one measures the ions which are produced when compounds are introduced into the flame. This detector is very sensitive to organic compounds, but it is insensitive to water and to pressure changes and flowrates in the carrier gas. It is ideal for general application, and is probably the most popular type of detector in use at present. A diagrammatic representation is shown in Fig. 35(a).

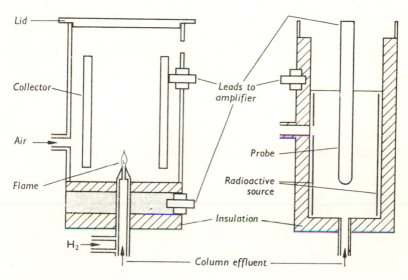

(a) Flame ionisation detector   (b) Argon detector (electron capture)

FIG. 35

The argon detector

In this detector, shown diagrammatically in Fig. 35(b), a radioactive source such as krypton 85 or strontium 90 excites the argon atoms of the carrier gas to a metastable state. When any substance with a lower ionisation potential than argon — and this includes most organic compounds and water — enters the detector, the energy stored in the metastabie argon atoms is transferred to the molecules of the substance, causing ionisation. This leads to an imbalance in the system which can be recorded.

The argon detector is relatively unaffected by temperature, pressure or flowrate changes, and it does not detect the inorganic and rare gases. However, it is very sensitive to organic compounds.

By altering the conditions within the detector (i.e. by changing the applied voltage or the ionising source) this apparatus can be made to function in different ways. The *electron capture* and *cross-section* detectors are both similar in design to the argon detector.

6.7 Amplifiers and recorders

Nearly all of the detectors discussed in the previous section give rise to a small electrical signal when components from the column pass through them. These signals are very weak and they are passed through an *amplifier* before being fed to the *recorder*.

Recorders consist of two basic parts: a strip of chart paper which moves along at a preselected speed, and a movable pen which is activated by the signal from the amplifier. The progress of a separation is therefore traced out as a series of peaks on the paper, the result being referred to as a chromatogram. A number of such chromatograms is shown in Plates 7 and 8.

6.8 Identification of substances in gas chromatography

The information from gas chromatographic separations is in the form of chromatograms. There is no chemical identification in most cases. The substances are identified by the time they take to emerge from the column, or more strictly by the distance on the chromatogram from the start of the separation to the peak given by that particular substance. Under constant conditions for a particular column, this is a reproducible and characteristic feature. In some cases, the volume of carrier gas emerging from the column before the given compound emerges, the retention volume, is used to identify the compound. The retention volume is a product of retention time and gas flowrate.

Substances can also be trapped out as they emerge from the column and be identified by any of the usual analytical procedures. In some very sophisticated machines, part of the effluent from the column is analysed directly by *mass spectrometry* to give both an identification and a check on the purity of the components.

6.9 Quantitative gas chromatography

Because the separating conditions in most chromatographs are reproducible, it is possible to convert the areas under the peaks in a chromatogram directly into quantitative measurements simply by comparing them with standard graphs of the appropriate compounds.

The usual way of measuring peak areas is by the product of (peak height × peak width at half peak height), which requires a considerable amount of measurement and calculating if a large number of chromatograms is involved, and is obviously time–consuming. Electronic devices known as *integrators* are available to perform this function automatically during the separation.

If only a good approximation is required, peak heights can be used for comparison.

6.10 Preparative gas chromatography

Gas chromatography is also a very valuable preparative tool, particularly where liquids are concerned. Large, ultrapure samples may be prepared by using longer, highly efficient columns. By scaling up the analytical apparatus and by designing the machines so that multiple injections of the same sample can be performed, even minute traces of contaminants in other materials can be isolated in sufficient quantities to allow identifying reactions to be conducted. For very large samples, air or nitrogen is generally the only safe and economic carrier gas, although helium is also used in the United States where it is much cheaper.

The progress of the separation in preparative gas chromatography is usually followed by passing the effluent from the column through a non-destructive detector, or splitting off a small percentage of the effluent through a detector and using the remainder to collect useful components.

7 Experimental Section

I Experiments on paper chromatography

Introduction

The procedure described for paper chromatography in Chapter 3 is that for commercially available apparatus. It is recommended that students should, as far as possible, familiarise themselves with this type of equipment. All the principles of paper chromatography can be demonstrated equally effectively using much simpler apparatus, of which a selection is shown in Fig. 36.

Note. Either Whatman No. 1 or Whatman No. 3 filter paper can be used for experiments 1 to 14.

Experiment 1 A simple separation of the indicators in screened methyl orange

Procedure

Place a drop of screened methyl orange in the centre of a piece of circular filter paper. Dry the spot carefully, hold it in ammonia fumes, and then add one small drop of water to the spot.

Result

Notice that the two indicators, methyl orange and bromothymol blue, travel outwards at different rates, the blue indicator moving faster than the yellow one.

Experiment 2 Separation of the components in several indicators by one-way chromatography

Technique

Prepare chromatograms by both the descending and ascending methods and compare the results.

Indicators required

The following pH indicators:

 - *a* Phenol red
 - *b* Bromophenol blue
 - *c* Congo red
 - *d* Screened methyl orange (a mixture of methyl orange and bromothymol blue).

Solvent Solvent 1.

Procedure

The procedures for both ascending and descending chromatography have been described in 3.1. In the ascending method use either the flat or

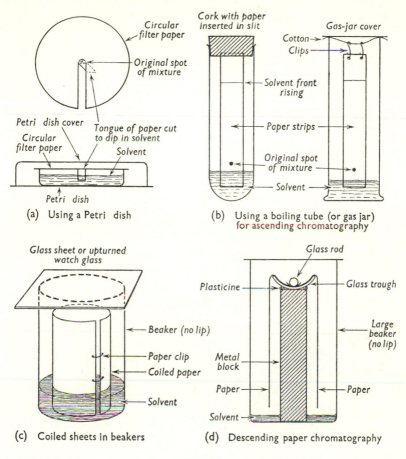

(a) Using a Petri dish

(b) Using a boiling tube (or gas jar) for ascending chromatography

(c) Coiled sheets in beakers

(d) Descending paper chromatography

FIG. 36

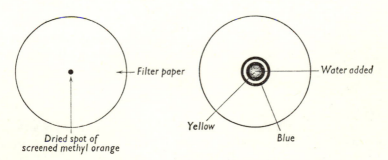

Filter paper

Dried spot of screened methyl orange

Water added

Yellow

Blue

FIG. 37

cylindrical paper according to convenience. Use separate drops of each indicator and a drop of a mixture of (a), (b), and (c). Before developing the paper, hold each spot over fumes from a bottle of 0.880 ammonia which will convert each indicator to the form it exhibits in alkaline solution.

If the indicators are allowed to run in the forms they exhibit in acid solution, the R_f values will be different. You can check this by a later experiment.

Results

After a suitable time, remove the chromatogram from the tank and mark the position of the solvent front. Dry the paper.

Notice that the spot of the mixture of indicators (a), (b), and (c) has separated into the separate indicators. Record the R_f values of (a), (b), and (c) which have been run separately and also their R_f values in the mixture. What conclusions do you draw from your results?

Notice that screened methyl orange has separated into its two components, one yellow and the other blue. Record their R_f values.

Experiment 3 To examine the nature of the components in several commercial inks by one-way chromatography

Technique

Prepare chromatograms by both the descending and ascending methods and compare the results.

Inks required

The following commercial inks:

Blue-black
Black
Green
Red
Brown
Royal Blue

Solvent Solvent 1.

Procedure

The procedures for ascending and descending chromatography have been described in 3.1. In the ascending method use either the flat or cylindrical paper according to convenience. Use separate drops of each ink and one drop of a mixture of brown and black inks.

Results

Notice that each commercial ink contains several pigments. Do you notice anything unusual about the pigments in brown ink?

After a suitable time, remove the paper carefully from the tank and mark the position of the solvent front. Dry the paper.

Record the R_f value of (a) the yellow pigment in red ink, (b) the red pigment in brown ink.

Experiment 4 To show that two-way chromatography of a mixture of inks produces better separation of all the components than one way chromatography

Technique

Ascending cylindrical method.

Inks required

Commercial inks:

    Brown
    Black

Solvents

Development in first direction: Solvent 1.
Development in second direction: Solvent 2.

Procedure

The method has been described in 3.1. Develop the spotted filter paper (one drop of each ink on a point a short distance in and up from one corner) in solvent 1 for a suitable time, remove the paper from the tank, dry it, turn it through 90°, and then develop it for the same time in solvent 2. For each run mark the position of the solvent front.

Results

Notice the more complete separation of components produced compared with the same mixture run by one-way chromatography (Experiment 3).

Experiment 5 Separation of metallic ions (Pb^{2+}, Ag^+ and Hg_2^{2+}) by one-way chromatography

Technique

Prepare chromatograms by both the ascending and descending methods and compare the results.

Solutions required

Molar aqueous solutions of:

    Lead nitrate
    Silver nitrate
    Mercurous nitrate.

Solvent Distilled (or deionised) water.

Procedure

The procedures for ascending and descending chromatography have been given in 3.1. Apply a drop of each separate solution and a drop of a mixture of all three.

A very neat separation by the ascending technique can be obtained using the apparatus of Fig. 36(b). A strip of filter paper is cut to such a size that it fits as shown into a boiling tube. The paper is spotted with the solutions as before and distilled (deionised) water is placed in the bottom of the tube. The filter paper is suspended in the solvent with its upper end pinned to the cork. The time of irrigation is such that the solvent front is almost to the top of the paper.

Location of spots

At the end of the run, the paper is removed from the boiling tube and dried carefully. It is then dipped into 0.25 molar potassium chromate solution when three colours will be seen: Pb^{2+} yellow, Ag^+ orange-red and Hg_2^{2+} orange. The surplus potassium chromate is washed off with water. If the paper is held over the top of an open 0.880 ammonia bottle, the colour of the silver chromate will fade while that of the mercurous compound will turn black.

Record the R_f values of the separated components in the mixture.

Experiment 6 Separation of metallic ions (Co^{2+}, Ni^{2+}, Cu^{2+}, Fe^{2+}) by one-way chromatography

Technique

Prepare chromatograms by the descending and ascending methods, and also include the ascending method in a boiling tube (Fig. 36(b)).

Solutions required

Concentrated aqueous solutions of:

- Cobalt sulphate
  Nickel sulphate
  Cupric sulphate
  Ferrous sulphate.

Solvent Solvent 3.

Procedure

The methods have been described in 3.1. Place one drop of the mixture on the paper. At the end of the run, remove the paper from the tank or boiling tube, dry it carefully and hold it in ammonia fumes until the smell of hydrochloric acid has gone.

Location of spots

The paper is dipped in a saturated solution of rubeanic acid (dithio-oxamide) in ethyl alcohol.

The colours produced are:

a Ni^{2+} blue
b Co^{2+} brown
c Cu^{2+} olive-green
d Fe^{2+} brownish-green

If desired, any 'background colour' on the paper can be removed by dipping in a 1 per cent aqueous solution of acetic acid.

Results

Measure and record the R_f values of the compounds. These should increase in the order (a) to (d).

Experiment 7 Separation of metallic ions (Bi^{3+}, Cd^{2+}, Cu^{2+}, Pb^{2+} and Hg^{2+} by one-way chromatography

Technique
Descending chromatography

Solutions required
Molar solutions of:

Bismuth chloride
Cadmium chloride
Cupric chloride
Lead chloride
Mercuric chloride

made up in dilute hydrochloric acid.

Solvent Solvent 4.

Procedure

The method has been given in 3.1. Put on one drop of each solution separately and one drop of the mixture of all five.

At the end of the run, remove the paper from the tank, mark the position of the solvent front, and dry the paper carefully.

Location of spots

Spray with (or dip in) a concentrated solution of dithizone in chloroform.

Colours produced

a Cu^{2+} brown
b Bi^{3+} purple
c Cd^{2+} purple
d Hg^{2+} pink

Lead ions can be located only by re-spraying with (or dipping in) concentrated aqueous rhodizonic acid (or sodium rhodizonate), the colour produced being deep blue.

Results

Measure and record R_f values which decrease in the order:
Cu^{2+}, Pb^{2+}, Bi^{3+}, Cd^{2+}, Hg^{2+}

Experiment 8 Separation of metallic ions (Bi^{3+}, Cd^{2+}, Cu^{2+}, Pb^{2+} and Hg^{2+}) on a circular filter paper

Method

Prepare concentrated aqueous solutions of bismuth nitrate, cadmium nitrate, cupric nitrate, lead nitrate and mercuric nitrate. Mix equal volumes of all five solutions and put one drop of the mixed solutions at the centre of a circular filter paper. Allow the spot to dry.

Into the bottom of a Petri dish (Fig. 36(a)) put about 15 cm³ of solvent 5 and cover the dish with another inverted dish of the same kind.

Form a wick on the filter paper by cutting a thin strip from the centre to the periphery of the paper. Place the paper on the rim of the lower dish (Fig. 36(a)) making sure that the wick is dipping in the solvent, and replace the top dish. Allow the solvent to reach the edge of the paper and then remove the paper and allow it to dry.

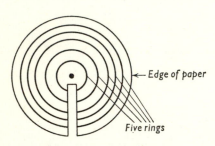

Edge of paper

Five rings

Fig. 38. The sprayed paper

Location

Hold the paper in an atmosphere of hydrogen sulphide until the rings of metallic sulphides are seen: Bi_2S_3 dark brown, CdS yellow, CuS chocolate brown, PbS black, HgS black.

Results

Ascertain the ring which corresponds to each sulphide by repeating the experiment with each separate solution.

Experiment 9 Separation of metallic ions (Ba^{2+}, Sr^{2+}, Ca^{2+}) by one-way chromatography

Technique

Descending chromatography.

Solutions required

Molar solutions of:

> Barium chloride or barium nitrate
> Strontium chloride or strontium nitrate
> Calcium chloride or calcium nitrate.

Solvent Solvent 6.

Procedure

The method has been given in 3.1. Spot with one drop of each solution separately and one drop of a mixture of all three.

Location of spots

At the end of the run, remove the paper from the tank, mark the position of the solvent front, dry it carefully, and spray with (or dip in) concentrated aqueous sodium rhodizonate to locate barium and strontium and with concentrated alcoholic alizarin to locate calcium.

Results

Barium ions move only very slowly in this solvent whilst calcium ions move just behind the solvent front. Strontium ions move close behind the calcium ions.

Record the R_f values.

Experiment 10 Separation of metallic ions (Fe^{3+}, Cr^{3+}, Al^{3+}) by one-way chromatography

Technique

Descending paper chromatography.

Solutions required

Molar solutions of:

> Ferric chloride
> Chromic chloride
> Aluminium chloride
made up in 4 M hydrochloric acid.

Solvent Solvent 7.

Procedure

The method is described in 3.1. Put on one spot of each solution separately and a streak of the mixture as shown in Fig. 39. Maintain low humidity in the tank by placing in the bottom of it a beaker of saturated potassium carbonate solution. After the stated time, remove the paper from the tank and dry it carefully.

68

Location of spots

Cut the paper into two parts as shown in Fig. 40. Spray part 1 with alcoholic alizarin solution after first holding the strip in ammonia fumes.

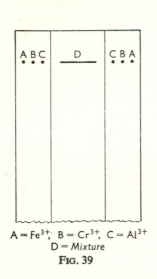

A = Fe^{3+}, B = Cr^{3+}, C = Al^{3+}
D = Mixture
Fig. 39

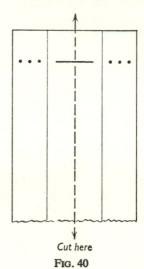

Cut here
Fig. 40

Spray part 2 with aqueous sodium peroxide solution followed by a solution of benzidine in acetic acid (taking care not to breathe in the fumes).

Results

Paper 1:

  Aluminium ions give a red lake
  Ferric ions give a purple lake.

Paper 2:

  Chromic ions give a deep blue band.

Experiment 11 The separation of halide anions

Technique

Descending chromatography.

Solutions required

Dissolve a few crystals each of sodium chloride, bromide and iodide in 100 cm^3 of distilled water.

Solvent Solvent 10.

Procedure

The procedure has been discussed in 3.1. Apply 1 drop of the mixture to the baseline. Develop the chromatogram until the solvent front is near the bottom of the paper. Remove the paper and allow it to dry.

Location of spots

Spray the paper with (or dip it in) 0.05 molar aqueous silver nitrate containing 4 per cent of a saturated solution of fluorescein in ethyl alcohol. Dip it in 2M nitric acid and finally in water. View under an ultraviolet lamp. The ions appear as dark spots on a fluorescent background, chloride (R_f 0.2, darkens rapidly), bromide (R_f 0.5) and iodide (R_f 0.7).

Experiment 12 Separation of several amino acids by one-way chromatography

Technique

Prepare chromatograms by both the ascending and descending methods and compare the results.

Solutions required

Concentrated aqueous solutions of:

Glycine
Aspartic acid
Glutamic acid
Tyrosine.

Solvent Solvent 8.

Procedure

The methods have been described in 3.1. Use one drop of each solution separately and one drop of a mixture of all four. At the end of the run, remove the paper from the tank, dry it and spray it with ninhydrin (dissolve 200 mg in 100 cm³ of acetone). Heat the paper in an oven at 80–100°C.

N.B. It is advisable to wear rubber gloves in this experiment because amino acids are present in perspiration. If gloves are not available, wash your hands well before spotting the paper and touch it only at the edges. Also, avoid getting ninhydrin on the fingers.

Results

The amino acids appear as blue-lilac spots. Record their R_f values.

Experiment 13 Separation of plastid pigments (chlorophylls, xanthophylls, carotenes) by one-way paper chromatography

Technique

Prepare chromatograms by ascending and descending chromatography and compare the results.

70

Solution required

Use the leaves of any green plant (e.g. spinach or grass) and extract the pigments by grinding with acetone and silver sand in a mortar. Remove the insoluble material by filtration.

Solvent Ether.

Procedure

The methods have been described in 3.1. Keep spotting the solution until the spot is distinctly green.

Results

You will see the separation of several coloured bands on the paper and there is therefore no need to use a locating reagent.

There is a green chlorophyll band, a yellow xanthophyll band and a greyish band which contains a mixture of decomposed chlorophylls and orange or yellow carotenes.

Experiment 14 Separation of the components produced when sucrose (cane sugar) is hydrolysed

Introduction

The molecule of sucrose consists of a glucose unit and a fructose unit linked together. When sucrose is warmed with a small quantity of a dilute mineral acid, the bond between the two units is broken and glucose and fructose are produced.

Sucrose $\xrightarrow{\text{dil. acid}}$ Glucose + Fructose

Technique

Prepare chromatograms by the descending method, preferably overnight.

Solutions required

Sucrose solution, obtained by dissolving one teaspoonful of the solid in 5 cm³ of distilled water. Also, 1 cm³ of M-hydrochloric acid.

Solvent Solvent 9.

Procedure

Put one drop of the solution on to the filter paper in three different places on the baseline (Fig. 41(*a*)). To the remainder of the solution, add the 1 cm³ of M-hydrochloric acid and warm the tube for a few minutes in a bunsen flame. Put one drop of the resulting solution on to the filter paper in three different places on the baseline (Fig. 41(*a*)). Allow all the spots to dry and then develop the chromatogram in the solvent stated for the given length of time. Remove the filter paper from the tank and allow it to dry.

Location of spots

Cut the filter paper into three parts (Fig. 41(*b*)) and use a different locating reagent for each part.

A: Dip the paper in a solution prepared by dissolving 2.5 cm³ of saturated aqueous silver nitrate in 10 cm³ of distilled water and making the volume to 500 cm³ with acetone. Allow the paper to dry and then spray it with a

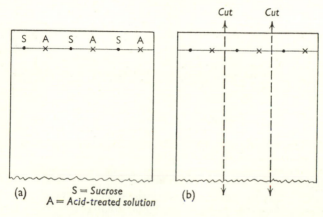

(a)   S = Sucrose   (b)
        A = Acid-treated solution

Fig. 41

solution made by dissolving 10 g of sodium hydroxide in the minimum volume of water and making the volume to 500 cm³ with ethyl alcohol.

B: Spray the paper with a solution of 1.5 per cent p-anisidine hydrochloride, dissolved in the minimum volume of methyl alcohol, and made up in n-butyl alcohol. Heat the paper at 100°C for 5 minutes in an oven.

C: Spray the paper with a solution of urea phosphate prepared as follows. To 100 cm³ of M-phosphoric acid in water-saturated ethyl alcohol, add 3 g of urea followed by 5 cm³ of ethyl alcohol to eliminate the aqueous phase. Heat the paper at 100°C for 5 minutes in an oven.

Results

Notice in A that the sucrose, glucose and fructose each appears as a brown spot. Record their R_G values (Fig. 42(*a*)).

You can keep this paper permanently if the background brown colour is removed by dipping the paper in 5 per cent aqueous sodium thiosulphate solution. Allow the paper to dry.

In B notice that the glucose appears as a brown spot while sucrose and fructose are yellow (Fig. 42(*b*)).

In C, notice that the spray reagent locates only the fructose and sucrose (blue spots) (Fig. 42(*c*)).

II Experiments on thin layer chromatography

The large number of materials used for thin layer work have already been mentioned in chapter four. For class demonstrations, however, most of the facets of this technique can be adequately demonstrated using only

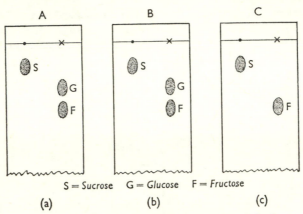

S = Sucrose   G = Glucose   F = Fructose

(a)   (b)   (c)

Fɪɢ. 42. Typical chromatograms showing hydrolysis

solid layers of silica gel. Experiments 16, 17 and 18 demonstrate this. If experience with other materials, such as alumina, cellulose, etc, is required, thin layers of these can be made in a similar manner.

Experiment 15 Preparation of small chromatoplates

Instructions for making six small plates on microscope slides. Do not attempt to make up more than this number at one time.

Take 3 g of Kieselgel G* powder and mix with 6 cm³ of deionised water in a mortar. Grind the two into a smooth paste.

Prepare six clean microscope slides and place them on a level surface.

Carefully transfer about 1 cm³ of the slurry on to each of the slides and, with the edge of another slide, smooth it evenly over the surface.** This must be done QUICKLY since Kieselgel G contains gypsum which hardens rapidly.

As the slides dry, it is generally found that some unevenness occurs, but this can be corrected by holding the slides between thumb and forefinger and gently waving them to and fro.

As an alternative to the above procedure, the slurry can be poured into a spray bottle and sprayed over the slides placed on a slightly inclined piece of wood or glass. Spray bottles MUST be washed out immediately after use. Spraying produces more even layers.

---

* Available from Anderman & Co. Ltd.

** Dipping the microscope slide into the mixture in order to apply a thin layer of sorbent is also very effective and rapid, e.g. for following the course of a column chromatographic separation such as the separation of steroids.

To activate the layers, the water introduced has to be removed. Heating in a steam oven for 30 minutes is usually sufficient. Appropriately less time is required if a hotter oven is available. Deactivated layers (i.e. containing a little water to help partition) can be produced either by exposing activated layers to a damp atmosphere for a short time or by allowing freshly prepared 'wet' layers to dry overnight in the laboratory.

Before applying samples, a thin strip of the layer is removed from the edge of the chromatoplate by means of a thumb nail.

If tanks specially designed for thin layer work are not available, an alternative is a suitable rimless beaker covered by a watch-glass. A piece of thick filter paper, slightly less than the height of the beaker and long enough to go about two-thirds of the way round the beaker, is introduced and the required solvent poured in to depth of about 1 cm, making sure that the paper is also saturated.

Experiment 16 Separation of ink pigments

Prepare activated silica gel plates by one of the methods described in Experiment 15.

(a) Ball-point pen inks. For this experiment, one black, one blue and one red ball-point pen, and three small filter papers (approx. 7 cm) are required. Scribble thoroughly with each pen on both sides of one of the filter papers, and then roll each into a loose ball and drop them separately into three boiling tubes, one for each colour. Extract some of the pigment by shaking with a little acetone and then place several drops of the solution on a line about 2 cm from one end of the plate. Develop in solvent 1. Note the compact nature of the spots and the range of pigments present in each ink. If an ultraviolet lamp is available, view the dry chromatoplate.

(b) Writing inks. Prepare the plates as before but use one drop of ordinary writing inks (see Experiment 3). Develop in solvent 1 and allow the solvent to reach nearly to the top of the slide. It will be found that drying the plates after development makes many more pigments visible.

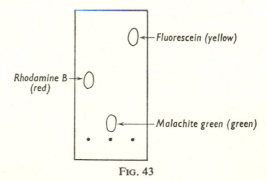

FIG. 43

Repeat this separation using deactivated silica gel plates, and compare the results with those obtained above and those of Experiment 3.

74

Experiment 17 Separation of dyestuffs on activated silica gel

Prepare a plate as described in Experiment 15. Activate and allow to cool. Place on the baseline a drop of a mixture of fluorescein and malachite green (each 0.1 per cent in methyl alcohol) and rhodamine B (0.05 per cent in methyl alcohol); filter the solution before use. Develop in solvent 11.

Experiment 18 Separation of amino acids on deactivated silica gel

Prepare two plates as described in Experiment 15, and leave them exposed to the air for a little while to allow deactivation. Place one drop of each of the amino acid solutions given in Experiment 12 on the baseline. Develop one plate in solvent 12a and the other in solvent 12b. Dry the plates and locate the substances as described in Experiment 12. Compare the separation achieved with the neutral solvent with that obtained with the solvent containing ammonia. What is the reason for this difference?

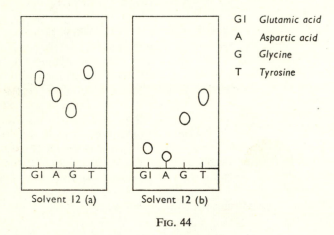

GI	Glutamic acid
A	Aspartic acid
G	Glycine
T	Tyrosine

Solvent 12 (a)   Solvent 12 (b)

Fig. 44

III Experiments on column chromatography

Experiment 19 Preparation of a column for chromatography

Select a piece of glass tube about 20 cm long and 2 cm in diameter. Take a short length of rubber tubing to join two short lengths of glass tubing (one of which is drawn out at one end), and assemble as shown in Fig. 25(a). Close the rubber tubing with a screw clip.

Place a filter disc (if available) into the bottom of the tube and then place over it some glass wool. Pour in some distilled water and remove air from the glass wool as shown in Fig. 25(b) using a long glass rod.

Weigh out about 12 g of finely divided chalk and make it into a thick slurry with distilled water (about 50 cm³) in a beaker. Pour this into the column until the latter is about two-thirds full. Keep the top surface of the chalk covered with a thin layer of water throughout all subsequent operations.

The column is now ready for the procedure described in Experiment 20.

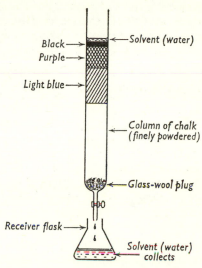

FIG. 45. Separation of the components of blue-black ink

Experiment 20 Separation of the components of blue-black ink by column chromatography on chalk

Preparation of the column

As described in Experiment 19.

Application of the mixture

Mix a few drops of ordinary blue-black ink with an equal volume of water and pour the liquid into the tube.

Notice that several coloured bands develop near the top of the column of adsorbent.

Development of the chromatogram

With the tap open, allow more distilled water to percolate through the column of chalk. Notice that the separation of the coloured bands gets better.

The coloured bands produced from a typical specimen of blue-black ink are shown in Fig. 45.

Experiment 21 Separation of two dyes by column chromatography on alumina

Preparation of the column

Prepare a column as directed in Experiment 19 except that alumina is used instead of chalk.

Application of the mixture

Add to the top of the column about 5 cm³ of an aqueous solution containing equal parts by weight of methylene blue and malachite green dyes. Notice that the blue dye is strongly adsorbed near the top of the column while the green dye is not so strongly adsorbed.

Development

Elute the column with distilled water (having the tap open). This will wash the green dye through the adsorbent and it can be collected. Now change the collection vessel and elute the blue dye with ethyl alcohol. This is a simple example of stepwise elution.

Experiment 22 Separation of metallic ions (Pb^{2+}, Ag^+ and Zn^{2+}) on an alumina column

Preparation of the column

Prepare the column as described in Experiment 19 except that alumina is used as the adsorbent.

Application of the mixture

To the top of the column add 5 cm^3 of a mixture of equal volumes of molar lead nitrate, silver nitrate and zinc nitrate.

Development

Develop the chromatogram with distilled water (50 cm^3) and then locate the compounds with ammonium sulphide solution (or hydrogen sulphide solution). The coloured bands formed will be:

   a Lead sulphide, black, near the top of the column
   b Silver sulphide, grey, intermediate
   c Zinc sulphide, off-white, near the bottom of the column.

Experiment 23 Separation of a mixture of ferric alum and cupric sulphate on an alumina column

Preparation of the column

Prepare the column as described in Experiment 19 except that alumina is used instead of chalk.

Application of the mixture

Add to the top of the column 5 cm^3 of a solution which contains molar quantities of ferric alum and cupric sulphate.

Development

Elute the column with about 50–60 cm^3 of distilled water (having the tap open). Notice the separation of a blue band (Cu^{2+}) below a brown band (Fe^{3+}). These bands can be further separated with more distilled water.

   If the bands are eluted with dilute potassium ferrocyanide solution (use 1–2 per cent solution), you will notice that the lower band becomes brown owing to the formation of cupric ferrocyanide (cf. the brown membrane of this material used in osmotic pressure experiments) while the upper band becomes a deep blue owing to the presence of ferric ferrocyanide (Prussian Blue).

Experiment 24 To demonstrate the separation of plastid pigments (chlorophylls, xanthophylls, and carotenes) by column chromatography on magnesia

Preparation of the column

Pack a column (Experiment 19) with a slurry of finely-powdered magnesium oxide (magnesia) in cyclohexane.

Preparation of the solution for analysis

Take 1 gram of fresh grass (or another green plant), cut it up into fine pieces in a mortar, add a little silver sand and grind for about 20 seconds. Place the ground material in a 50 cm³ stoppered flask, add 5 cm³ of warm cyclohexane, stopper and shake the flask vigorously for 20–30 seconds. Allow the flask to stand for about 10 minutes. Remove the green solution by means of a pipette and add it to the column prepared as directed above. Notice that bands of coloured compounds begin to separate.

Development

Add more of the pure solvent to the top of the column, open the tap, and allow the chromatogram to develop. Notice the separation of bands

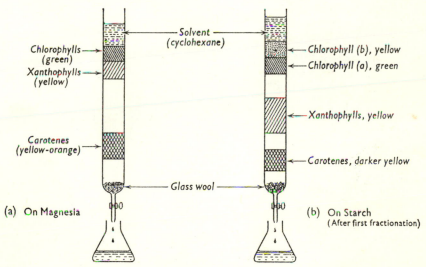

FIG. 46. Separation of the pigments in a grass extract

containing chlorophylls (strongly adsorbed), xanthophylls, and carotenes.

Repeat the experiment using starch as adsorbent. Is there any difference in the extent of adsorption of the chlorophyll?

Elute off the various coloured bands, add a little more cyclohexane to the combined eluate, and refractionate the mixture on a new column of starch, developing the chromatogram with cyclohexane. Notice the separation of the two chlorophylls (*a*) and (*b*), see Fig. 46(*b*).

Similar separations can be effected for the following substances on alumina columns.

(a) 5 cm³ of a filtered 40 per cent solution of butter in benzene, the chromatogram being developed with benzene. (Compare this with a similar chromatogram for margarine.)

(b) 5 cm³ of a solution obtained by extracting a chopped up carrot root with petrol/ether (highly inflammable), the chromatogram being developed with petrol/ether.

IV Experiments on gas chromatography

Experiment 26 Construction of a simple apparatus for gas chromatography
See Fig. 47.

Experiment 27 To demonstrate the separation of the chloromethanes

Pack the U tube with Celite (80–120 mesh) which has been previously treated with silicone oil, tapping the tube at intervals to ensure uniform packing. Then assemble the apparatus as shown in Fig. 47. Ignite the coal

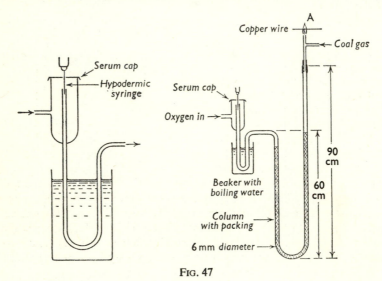

Fig. 47

gas at the orifice A and obtain a luminous flame 5–8 cm high. Pass oxygen at a pressure of about 20 kN/m²(3 lbf/in²) (or air at a slightly higher pressure) through the apparatus and re-adjust the flame to a convenient height. Clamp a piece of copper wire in the flame as shown. Having ascertained that the water in the beaker is boiling gently, inject 0.02 cm³ of the sample (equal volumes of ethyl chloride, methylene dichloride and chloroform) into the tube by means of a hypodermic syringe, noting the time on a stop-watch.

The emergence of each compound from the column is shown by the green colouration of the flame (by the copper halides formed). The order in which the compounds appear is ethyl chloride, methylene dichloride and chloroform. Note the time at which each compound starts to emerge and how long it takes to come through.

Experiment 28 To demonstrate the separation of some more compounds

The apparatus is as shown in Fig. 48. A sample of Tide detergent, which has previously been thoroughly dried, is sieved so as to obtain the particles of 60–100 mesh, and the column is then packed with this material, tapping the column from time to time to ensure uniform packing. The column is then connected to the rest of the apparatus and a stream of hydrogen passed through the apparatus until all the air has been removed (this is VERY IMPORTANT, or an explosion might result on ignition); the hydrogen is then ignited to give an almost colourless flame.

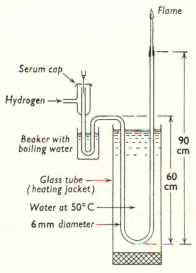

FIG. 48

Fill the heating jacket with water at 60°C and make sure that the water in the beaker is boiling steadily.

When the temperature of the water jacket has fallen to 50°C, inject 0.02 cm³ of the sample (a mixture of equal volumes of diethyl ether, carbon disulphide, benzene and carbon tetrachloride) in through the serum cap, noting the time on a stopwatch. As each compound emerges from the column it imparts a characteristic colour to the flame. The order of elution is diethyl ether (bright yellow flame), carbon disulphide (light blue flame), benzene (luminous smoky flame) and carbon tetrachloride (blue, changing to yellow smoky flame).

CAUTION. Students should note that hydrogen and oxygen can form a mixture which is dangerously explosive when ignited.

8 Preparation of Solvents for use in Chromatography

The solvents used in chromatography should be made up *carefully* in a graduated measuring cylinder, and should be *shaken well* before use.

Solvent 1

n-Butyl alcohol	3 volumes
Ethyl alcohol	1 volume
2M-ammonia	1 volume

Solvent 2

Water (distilled)	15 volumes
Ethyl alcohol	3 volumes
Ammonium sulphate (saturated aqueous)	2 volumes

Solvent 3

Acetone	17 volumes
Water (distilled)	1 volume
Conc. hydrochloric acid	2 volumes

Solvent 4

n-Butyl alcohol saturated with 3M hydrochloric acid. Prepare this solvent by shaking up equal volumes of the two components in a separating funnel. Reject the lower aqueous layer and use the upper (organic) phase for chromatography.

Solvent 5

Acetone	2 volumes
Tertiary butyl alcohol	2 volumes
Dil. nitric acid	1 volume

Solvent 6

Pyridine containing 1 per cent potassium thiocyanate and 20 per cent distilled water (by weight).

Solvent 7

Glacial acetic acid	3 volumes
Dry methyl alcohol*	1 volume

Solvent 8

n-Butyl alcohol	6 volumes
Glacial acetic acid	1 volume
Water (distilled)	2 volumes

(Alternatively, the composition of this solvent can be 8:1:8 by volume, respectively, for the components listed.)

Solvent 9

Ethyl acetate	9 volumes
Glacial acetic acid	2 volumes
Water (distilled)	2 volumes

Solvent 10

Pyridine	9 volumes
Water	1 volume

Solvent 11

Methyl ethyl ketone	2 volumes
Acetic acid	2 volumes
Isopropyl alcohol	1 volume

Solvent 12

(*a*) Ethyl alcohol	7 volumes	(*b*) Ethyl alchol	7 volumes
Water	3 volumes	33% ammonia	3 volumes

* Reflux commercial methyl alcohol with quicklime for 5–6 hr. and then distil off the alcohol. When refluxing, exclude moisture by attaching a calcium chloride tube to the top of the condenser.

Index